WESTWARD MOVEMENT

BUFFALO BILL, *Stevenson*
DANIEL BOONE, *Stevenson*
DAVY CROCKETT, *Parks*
JESSIE FREMONT, *Wagoner*
JED SMITH, *Burt*
JIM BOWIE, *Winders*
JIM BRIDGER, *Winders*
KIT CARSON, *Stevenson*
LOTTA CRABTREE, *Place*
MERIWETHER LEWIS, *Bebenroth*
NARCISSA WHITMAN, *Warner*
SACAGAWEA, *Seymour*
SAM HOUSTON, *Stevenson*
TECUMSEH, *Stevenson*
WILL CLARK, *Wilkie*
WILLIAM HENRY HARRISON, *Peckham*
ZEB PIKE, *Stevenson*

THE NATION DIVIDED

ABE LINCOLN, *Stevenson*
BEDFORD FORREST, *Parks*
CLARA BARTON, *Stevenson*
DAVID FARRAGUT, *Long*
HARRIET BEECHER STOWE, *Widdemer*
JEB STUART, *Winders*
JULIA WARD HOWE, *Wagoner*
MARY TODD LINCOLN, *Wilkie*
RAPHAEL SEMMES, *Snow*
ROBERT E. LEE, *Monsell*
TOM JACKSON, *Monsell*
U. S. GRANT, *Stevenson*

RECONSTRUCTION and EXPANSION

ALECK BELL, *Widdemer*
BOOKER T. WASHINGTON, *Stevenson*
JOHN WANAMAKER, *Burt*

LUTHER BURBANK
MARIA MITCHELL, *Melin*
MARK TWAIN, *Mason*
MARY MAPES DODGE, *Mason*
SITTING BULL, *Stevenson*
SUSAN ANTHONY, *Monsell*
TOM EDISON, *Guthridge*

TURN of the CENTURY

ANNIE OAKLEY, *Wilson*
DAN BEARD, *Mason*
GEORGE CARVER, *Stevenson*
GEORGE DEWEY, *Long*
GEORGE EASTMAN, *Henry*
JAMES WHITCOMB RILEY, *Mitchell*
JANE ADDAMS, *Wagoner*
JOHN PHILIP SOUSA, *Weil*
JULIETTE LOW, *Higgins*
KATE DOUGLAS WIGGIN, *Mason*
THE RINGLING BROTHERS, *Burt*
ROBERT PEARY, *Clark*
TEDDY ROOSEVELT, *Parks*
WALTER REED, *Higgins*
WILBUR AND ORVILLE WRIGHT, *Stevenson*
WILL AND CHARLIE MAYO, *Hammontree*

IN RECENT YEARS

AMELIA EARHART, *Howe*
A. P. GIANNINI, *Hammontree*
BABE RUTH, *Van Riper*
ERNIE PYLE, *Wilson*
FRANKLIN ROOSEVELT, *Weil*
HENRY FORD, *Aird-Ruddiman*
JIM THORPE, *Van Riper*
KNUTE ROCKNE, *Van Riper*
LOU GEHRIG, *Van Riper*
RICHARD BYRD, *Van Riper*
WILL ROGERS, *Van Riper*
WOODROW WILSON, *Monsell*

William Fargo

Young Mail Carrier

Illustrated by James Ponter

William

Fargo

Young Mail Carrier

By Katharine E. Wilkie

 THE **BOBBS-MERRILL** COMPANY, INC.
A SUBSIDIARY OF HOWARD W. SAMS & CO., INC.
Publishers • INDIANAPOLIS • NEW YORK

To My Students of 1960-1961
who helped with research
for this book
and
To Jock
who named Trez

Illustrations

Numerous smaller illustrations

Contents

Books by Katharine E. Wilkie

GEORGE ROGERS CLARK: BOY OF THE OLD NORTHWEST
MARY TODD LINCOLN: GIRL OF THE BLUEGRASS
SIMON KENTON: YOUNG TRAIL BLAZER
WILL CLARK: BOY IN BUCKSKINS
WILLIAM FARGO: YOUNG MAIL CARRIER
ZACK TAYLOR: YOUNG ROUGH AND READY

★ ★ William

Fargo

Young Mail Carrier

Independence
Day

"ALL ABOARD!" Father sang out.

"Wait," William Fargo called. "Aren't you forgetting something?"

The seven-year-old boy handed the big wicker lunch basket up to his brother Rome, aged five. The younger boy passed it across the back of the seat to Father, who tucked it under his legs.

The boys had watched Mother pack that basket. They knew everything that was in it. There were slices of spicy, sugary ham. There were two loaves of golden-brown bread still warm from the oven. There was a huckleberry pie which had not yet cooled from baking. There

11

was a jar of blackberry jam. There was a smaller one of crabapple jelly. There was crisp, crunchy watermelon pickle. There was even a jar of cool sweet apple cider.

William climbed over the wheel and took his place beside Rome. The two boys knelt in the straw of the wagon bed. They leaned their chins on their folded arms against the back of the seat.

Mother, with little Chan in her lap, smiled back at them. "Are you comfortable?" she asked.

"Let's go!" William begged. "I like to travel and see things."

Father laughed. He shook the reins over the horse's head. Zilpah moved off at a slow trot. The wagon rolled behind her.

"You will never make a farmer, William," Father said. "You can't wait."

"I don't want to be a farmer," his eldest son told him. "Planting and harvesting are too slow for me. I like to keep moving."

"Now you're being foolish," Mother told him. "Planting and harvesting are a part of living. They must go on."

William did not reply. He did not want to hurt Mother's feelings, but he did not like farming very much.

The Fargo family lived on a small farm in mid-state New York. Today was July 4, 1825. They were going to the Independence Day celebration at the near-by village of Pompey.

By now the Fargos had reached the Great Western Turnpike. Every day settlers came from the east along this route and pushed farther into the wilderness to the west.

Today the turnpike was filled with wagons full of people, riders on horseback, and men and boys on foot. Once in a while a carriage rolled by. Everyone was on his way to Pompey.

At last the Fargos reached the edge of the little town. William hardly knew the place. It did not always look like this. There were dozens of wagons and horses in the shady grove where Father stopped.

"Whoa-a!" Father called. He pulled on the reins, and Zilpah stopped. "Climb down, boys. I'll help your mother."

William was the first to reach the ground. Rome was close behind him. The brothers waited first on one foot and then on the other for their parents to get down.

Father leaped over the left front wheel. Then he held out his arms for little Chan. After that he helped Mother down.

"You take the lunch basket," Mother said. "I will carry Chan."

Father laughed. "I hope I'm strong enough to cary a basket and a baby at the same time."

The Fargos started toward the center of town. They could hear music playing and people cheering. Behind them Zilpah gave a loud neigh.

William ran back to her. "Father, we must feed her," he cried.

Mr. Fargo reached into the back of the wagon and brought out a feedbag and fastened it to the horse's muzzle. Soon she was champing away contentedly at her oats.

Then Father took Mother by the arm. They walked so fast that William and Rome almost had to run to keep up with them.

In a few minutes they came to the town square where the crowd was gathered. Big white frame houses stood at the edge of the grassy space. At one side was a small general store. Next to it was a tavern, in front of which a large sign said, "Entertainment for Man and Beast."

Today, William noticed, there were rows of benches on the green. Many persons were already in their seats. William and Rome slipped into a bench behind Father and Mother.

The platform facing the benches was draped

in red, white, and blue bunting. A huge American flag with twenty-four stars on a blue field waved in the breeze.

"I know what the stripes stand for," Rome whispered to William. "The thirteen states which were once the thirteen colonies."

William nodded. "The stars are for all the states," he said. "Father says there will be others someday. People are going west all the time now, he says."

Just then a band burst into a lively march. William could hardly keep his feet still. He and Rome kept time to the music. There was so much to see and hear today!

"I wish I had two heads," William said.

Rome giggled. "I'd rather have one of those little flags." He pointed to several boys in the next row, who were waving small American flags. He and William looked at the flags wistfully. "I wonder where they came from?"

Just then William felt a hand on his shoulder. He turned to see a kind-looking stranger standing beside him, holding a handful of flags.

"Would you boys like to have a flag?" he asked.

"Yes, sir!" William and Rome exclaimed.

The man handed them two flags. "I guess the baby is too little," he said with a laugh.

"Thank you, sir," the boys said.

Father turned his head to see what was going on. He and the man stared at each other for a minute. Then they began to laugh.

"Will Fargo!" the stranger said. "I haven't seen you since the war."

"Hugh Bell!" Father cried. "I might have known you would come west."

The other nodded. "I'm going farther, too. The East is too crowded for me any more. I'm on my way to Buffalo to find work."

Up on the platform a tall man in a long black coat rose from a chair and walked across to the speaker's stand.

Mother placed a finger on her lips. "Sh-h!" she said, looking at Father.

William almost laughed aloud. It seemed strange for Mother to remind Father to be quiet.

"Sh-h!" she said again. "The minister is about to begin."

18

After the prayer was over, another man came to the stand. A heavy gold watch chain hung across the front of his vest.

"That is our Congressman," Father whispered to William.

William knew exactly what Father meant. A Congressman represented the people who were here today at Washington, the United States capital. He represented Father, Mother, and even him, William George Fargo.

The boy sat up very straight. That was his Congressman and his flag yonder.

William did not understand much that the Congressman was saying. His mind kept wandering. The day was hot, and a fly buzzed near him. Before long he felt drowsy. He thought about the covered basket in the wagon under the trees.

Then he began to hear some of the speaker's words: "When in the course of human events, it becomes necessary . . . to assume . . . the . . . station . . . We hold these truths to be self-evident . . . the pursuit of happiness——"

Of course! The Declaration of Independence! Father kept a copy of it in the Bible on the table at home. He had read the Declaration aloud and talked about it many times.

Today was the birthday of the Declaration of Independence. It was forty-nine years old. All these folks had come to the birthday party. These thoughts went through William's mind.

At last the speaker sat down. There was a round of applause. Then the people in the audience rose to their feet. The band began to play again. Families went off in little groups. It was lunch time at last.

Father turned to the man behind them. "Is anyone with you, Hugh?"

The man shook his head. "Neither chick nor child," he said.

Father threw a friendly arm across his shoulders. "Then you shall eat with us."

Mother nodded. "Please do. We have more than enough."

Soon the Fargos and their guest were sitting in the shade under a giant oak tree. The food was spread out on a white tablecloth. Little Chan lay on an old coverlet and waved his arms and cooed happily.

Father bowed his head and said grace.

"For food and friends and home and heaven,
   For all Thy gifts in mercy given,
   We thank Thee, Lord. Amen."

Mother passed the ham. She cut the bread and the pie. Father poured the cider. Mr. Bell joked and laughed as if he had known the Fargo family forever. It was a happy time for all of them.

At last the boys stretched out on the grass, too full to eat another crumb. They were even too full to talk, so they listened to Father and Mr. Bell. The men talked about old times when they were in the army together during the War of 1812.

"Those were great days, but I am glad they are over," Hugh Bell said. "This nation has grown by leaps and bounds since the war ended. Its boundaries are pushing on. After I have been in Buffalo a while, I intend to push on, too. You had better bring your family and go west with me, Fargo."

Father shook his head. "I've put down my roots here. This is the place for me. I came here when I was sixteen. This is good farm land, and I like farming."

"America is a big country," Hugh Bell told him. "This isn't the only farming land. Settlers are streaming into the wilderness and across the Mississippi River. A lot of them followed Daniel Boone out there."

Father puffed away at his pipe. "There will be still more people heading west when the Erie Canal opens soon."

Mr. Bell nodded. "You're right. There's no telling what lies out yonder. Many a man will make his fortune in the West."

William looked up at Mr. Bell. His father's friend made the West seem the most exciting place in the whole world.

Father reached over and patted Mother's hand. "I've already found my fortune," he said. "My wife Tacy and I are cousins. Our people came across the ocean from Wales nearly two hundred years ago. I came here from Connecticut, and that's enough traveling for me."

"It's not for me," William said to himself. "I wonder what the West is like."

"We Fargos are a quiet, home-loving lot," Father added. "We will stay here."

Hugh Bell rose to his feet. "Every man must

23

choose for himself," he said. "Now it's time for me to say good-by. You may want to stay here, Will, but this youngster——"

He laid a hand on William's rumpled hair. William's heart skipped a beat. Somehow this man knew how he felt.

"This boy will never be a farmer," Hugh Bell said. "He will be too busy going places and doing things. You wait and see."

Off to Syracuse

"PLEASE, FATHER, may I go to Syracuse with you?" William asked eagerly.

Father hesitated. He looked at William without saying a word. Then he looked at Rome. William was taller than Rome.

"You boys are like stairsteps," Father said, smiling. "Do you suppose you'll ever grow to be the same size?"

William wiggled in his chair. "I'll be good if you take me," he promised.

"Well," Father said slowly, "I'll tell you what I've decided to do."

For some reason he sounded excited. His sons

25

pricked up their ears. Mother stopped stirring
the kettle hanging over the hearth. Even little
Chan in his high chair seemed to be listening.

Father nodded his head. "Yes, I've made up
my mind. I'm going to take the whole family."

William and Rome sprang to their feet. They
could hardly believe their ears.

"Hurrah!" William cried. "Everybody's going."

"Even Chan?" Rome asked.

Father smiled over their heads at Mother. "I
think he's a little young to leave behind, don't
you, Mother?"

Mother smiled back. William noticed that her
cheeks were as pink as the wild rose that grew
at the front door. Then a little frown came on
her forehead.

"Do you think we can afford to go?" she asked.

"We can't afford to stay home," Father answered. "The opening of the Erie Canal is one
of the biggest things that have ever happened

in this country. We must see the boats as they go eastward. It will be a grand sight. The boys will tell their children and even their grandchildren about it someday."

Mother seemed satisfied. "I think the trip is a wonderful idea," she said.

"We'll stop at Cousin Dora's house for the night," Father said. "She has always made me feel that we are welcome and wanted. We'll take along a ham and some jars of your jellies and pickles, Tacy. Pack a basket of food that we can eat along the way. Taverns are expensive. Besides, your food is better than theirs."

The next morning William was awake before the sun came up. With the first gray streaks of dawn he heard their old rooster crowing in the barnyard. For once Mother did not have to call him. He bounced out of bed and shook his brother Rome as hard as he could.

"Get up! Get up! We're going to Syracuse!"

Downstairs Mother was hurrying, hurrying, hurrying. She had just finished bathing little Chan. Now he lay in his crib as if he were watching the family get ready.

Mother had on her second-best dress. She had folded her best one carefully along with Father's Sunday suit in the old carpetbag. She had tucked in clean clothes for the boys, too.

Now she pointed to the shirts and pants on the big bed. "Hurry into them," she told her sons, "but wash your faces first. We have no time to waste. There's a long trip ahead of us."

A few minutes later the Fargos were gathered about the breakfast table.

"Eat a big breakfast," Father told them. "We won't have another hot meal until we reach Cousin Dora's house tonight."

William spooned up his oatmeal. He thought he might as well be eating sawdust. Who cared about food on such a day as this. Then he decided to have a second bowl. He poured thick rich cream over the cereal and added little lumps of maple sugar to sweeten it. Syracuse or no Syracuse, this oatmeal was good.

Before long the Fargos were rolling along in the family wagon behind old Zilpah. They were following the Great Western Turnpike toward Pompey, on their way to Syracuse.

William grinned at Rome. "Are we dreaming? Shall I pinch you to make sure it's true?"

"No" Rome said hastily. "Please don't!"

Mother looked back at them with a little frown. "Be quiet, boys. You're much too noisy."

Father shook the reins over Zilpah's back. He and Mother began to talk. Baby Chan talked to himself. In the back of the wagon the boys were still for at least two minutes.

It was still early morning when they rode through the village of Pompey. The place was deserted. Smoke rose slowly from the chimneys of several houses, but William did not see a soul. There were only two wagons and a saddle horse tied outside Handy's Tavern. Practically everyone in town was on his way to Syracuse.

Cousin Dora lived on a farm five miles from Syracuse. She was feeding her chickens when the wagonful of Fargos rolled up the lane in the middle of the afternoon.

The old woman shaded her eyes with her hand. Then she gave a glad little cry. "It's Will Fargo and his family! What a surprise this is! Get down and come into the house."

Inside the house Cousin Dora put her hands on her hips and looked admiringly at her young relatives. They were munching cookies which she had taken from a gaily-painted tin box in the corner cupboard in the kitchen.

"My, my! How you boys have grown," she said. "I haven't see you since right after Chancellor Livingston was born."

William hid a smile. It sounded odd to hear Chan called by his whole name.

Cousin Dora was still talking. "You're the tallest of all, William. You'll be a grown young man before I know it."

William sat up very straight. Cousin Dora made him feel important. He liked her gentle voice. He liked the scent of lavender about her. He liked her cookies, too.

"So you're all going to the big doings at Syracuse," she said. "That will be exciting."

"And you're going with us," Father said. "We have plenty of room for you in the wagon."

"Oh, I couldn't go!" she protested. "Who would feed my chickens and my cow?"

"A neighbor is taking care of our stock," Father said. "You must have neighbors, too."

Cousin Dora rubbed her chin. "Sam Brown down the road isn't going. He says he would rather hear the brook ripple past his house than see all the water in all the man-made ditches in the world."

Father laughed. "I agree with him, but tomorrow is special. I'm sure he will do your chores, Cousin Dora."

"I think the barges will come down the canal tomorrow," the old woman said. She was thinking aloud. "I heard the cannon four days ago."

"Cannon?" William asked.

"Yes, cannon," Cousin Dora told him. "When the barges left Buffalo on Lake Erie, the militia fired several cannon. When the sound reached other points along the canal, other cannon were fired. The ones at Syracuse sounded like thunder. They scared my poor cow so that she didn't give half the milk she usually does. I hear the signal went across the state in less than two hours. Folks all along the way will be waiting for the boats. They are the first boats to come down the Erie Canal."

"Why, it's just like the tomtoms people say the natives use in Africa," William said. "They're used for signalling, too."

"Well, we don't live in a jungle," Cousin Dora chuckled. "New York State is an up-and-coming place. If we just had some good roads——"

"That's why the Erie Canal was built," Father said. "Waterways are cheaper than roads."

"And smoother," Mother added. 'That corduroy road we drove over for several miles today was anything but smooth."

"Maybe so, but it will last," Father said. "Those logs laid side by side may make traveling rough, but they'll be there for years."

That evening as they sat at supper, a horseman rode up to the door. Without getting off his horse, he blew a blast on a horn. Everyone jumped up from the supper table and ran outside to gather around him.

"What is it?" asked Cousin Dora excitedly.

"The barges from Buffalo should reach Syracuse before noon tomorrow."

Cousin Dora sniffed. "They're taking long enough," she said. "They left Buffalo four days ago, didn't they?"

"Yes, but they're carrying important people," the rider said, winking at Father. "You can't hurry Governor DeWitt Clinton. He and his party are wined and dined at every spot along the way. I should think he would be worn out from eating and making speeches."

He wheeled his horse and waved his hand. "I must be going," he said. "It would never do for anyone in the countryside to miss the news." He galloped down the road.

Noah's Ark

EARLY the next morning the Fargo family and Cousin Dora were on their way to Syracuse. William thought everyone in central New York must be going to the same place. The narrow road was crowded with men on horseback and families in wagons. A few persons were trudging along the side of the road on foot. Rich and poor had turned out for the great event.

It was mid-morning when the Fargos finally reached Syracuse. William looked about at all the people. The crowd at the Independence Day celebration seemed small now. He wondered where all the people had come from.

"I didn't know there were so many people in the world," he told Father.

Father smiled. "The world is a big place."

An awful thought came to William. "What if the barges have already passed!"

"They haven't," Father assured him. "Don't you see all the people going the same way. They're on their way to the canal."

William felt better. He would hate to miss the sight he had come for.

The Fargos and Cousin Dora followed the crowd until they came to the banks of the canal. A long dock had been built right down to the edge of the water. Above and below the dock a towpath had been built on either side of the stream. The canal stretched away in a straight line as far as one could see. William noticed that the water was flowing east.

"Just think!" Cousin Dora said. "They have been eight years building the canal. That water flowing by us came all the way from Lake Erie. It will flow into the Hudson River and then into the Atlantic Ocean. That is a long way."

William wrinkled up his nose. "What do I smell?" he asked.

"Salt," his father replied. "Syracuse and the neighboring village of Saline have big salt deposits. That is why the salt manufacturers wanted the canal to come through here. They can ship their salt east or west."

"Here they come!" someone shouted.

William stood on tiptoe and stretched his neck. Far in the distance came the first canalboat. William knew it was called the "Seneca Chief." The governor of the state along with other well-known men would be on it.

The flotilla drew nearer and nearer. There were "Oh's!" and "Ah's" from the people as the boats floated along.

For a moment William wondered what moved

them. Then he saw four sturdy mules hitched to the leading boat by a long rope. As the mules walked along the towpath, guided by a rider on the back of the first one, the barge moved slowly along the canal.

On the top of the barge sat Governor DeWitt Clinton. Several other gentlemen in fine clothes sat beside him. They waved their hats and bowed as the barge passed the long dock.

There was a band on the dock, playing a march. The men wore red and white uniforms, and William thought their music was much better than the music he had heard in Pompey on Independence Day.

As the "Seneca Chief" moved down the canal, William looked upstream to see the next boat. He began to spell out its name. " 'S-u-p-e-r——' "

" 'Superior,' " Father said. "Do you know what that means, William?"

William didn't hear him. He was already looking at the third barge. " 'Commodore Perry!' " he exclaimed. "Wasn't he the man who won the Battle of Lake Erie?"

Cousin Dora nodded. "So he was. And here comes the 'Buffalo.' "

The last barge was called the "Noah's Ark."

"That's an odd name for a boat," William said.

By this time the crowd was moving along the canal to the spot where the first boat had come to a stop. Everyone wanted to hear the governor speak. Somehow in the hustle and bustle William became separated from the rest of his family. There were so many people everywhere. They all pushed and shoved until he grew tired and hot. At last he gave up trying to find his family. He could hunt them later. Right now, he decided, he would get a closer look at the "Noah's Ark," which lay near by.

"That's the most interesting boat of them all," someone said beside him.

William looked up quickly and saw Mr. Hugh Bell smiling down at him. He almost shouted with joy. He liked the tall, smiling man who was his father's friend.

"What are you doing here, sir?" he asked.

Mr. Bell nodded toward the boats. "I came on one of them," he said. "There must be men to work on the boats, as well as the fine gentlemen who ride with the governor."

"You really came all the way from Buffalo?" William asked.

"Yes," Mr. Bell said.

"And you are going all the way to Albany?"

"Farther than that," Mr. Bell said. "Governor Clinton has two kegs of water with him from Lake Erie. He intends to sail right down the Hudson River to New York Bay. Then he will empty the water from Lake Erie into the Atlantic Ocean."

William gave a long whistle. "That's quite a trip, isn't it?"

"Three hundred and sixty-three miles," Mr. Bell told him. "It's an expensive trip, too. The building of the Erie Canal cost New York State about $7,000,000."

The boy's eyes grew bigger. "Where will they ever get that much money?"

"From the taxpayers," Mr. Bell said. "From your father and his neighbors and all the other folks in New York State. But don't you worry.

42

The canal will pay for itself quicker than you think it will."

He glanced down and saw that William was not listening. "There are many thing more interesting than miles and dollars," he said. "Come with me, and I'll show you some of them."

He took William by the hand and led his across the towpath and up the gangplank of the "Noah's Ark." "Come on," he said.

"Are we really going on board?" asked William.

"We certainly are," Mr. Bell said, giving his hand a squeeze. "We'd better hurry, too. Those animals must be getting hungry."

William followed his friend onto the deck of the "Noah's Ark." Then he followed him down a narrow stairs to a cabin below.

The first thing he noticed was that the cabin smelled much like the inside of the barn at home. He could not see too well after the bright autumn sunlight outdoors. He blinked his eyes several times until they grew used to the dimness. Then he opened them wide and stared as hard as he could. He was amazed by what he saw.

In a large wire cage at the far end of the cabin were two great eagles. A sign on the door of the cage read *Danger*. William did not have to read the word to notice the eagles' cruel beaks and sharp talons. He kept at a safe distance from the cage.

"Fierce, aren't they?" said Mr. Bell. "I'd be fierce, too, if I were cooped up like that instead of being free."

Now William was exploring farther. On a pile of clean straw lay two gentle little fawns. They looked up at him with eyes that were almost human. William smiled.

"Pet, them," Mr. Bell urged. "They won't bite."

William reached out a careful hand. The fawns felt as soft as the little calf at home, and they were much prettier.

As William walked along looking at the fawns, he bumped into something.

"Umph!" a voice said.

William looked round quickly and found himself face to face with a tall, copper-colored boy about twelve years old. The boy was wearing deerskin pants and a deerskin jacket, and at his side was another boy like him who was dressed in the same way.

William's eyes opened wider still. He turned to Mr. Bell. "Are they real Indians?" he said.

The boys smiled and nodded their heads.

"They can understand me!" William cried.

"They understand better than they speak," Mr. Bell said. "They know only a few words of English. Governor Clinton brought them along with the animals. Products of the West for the East to see, he says."

"What will become of them?" William asked.

"Oh, they will be taken back to their people,"

Mr. Bell said. "Come along now. You haven't seen Bingo yet."

One of the Indian boys stepped forward and poked a long stick at what William had thought was a pile of black furs in one corner. A half-grown bear rose to its feet and took a few steps. It came to a halt as the Indian boy waved the stick. William watched eagerly as the bear went through its tricks. Then it walked back to its corner and fell asleep once more.

The Indian boy turned to William. His white teeth shone in a friendly smile.

"You like?"

"I like very much," William answered.

The bear trainer tapped the other Indian on the shoulder. "My brother—and I—like you," he said with another smile.

William felt warm and happy. He turned to Mr. Bell. "Please tell them that I like them, too."

Hugh Bell spoke a few words in a tongue that

William had never heard before. The boys nodded. They seemed to understand.

"Now let's get to work," said Mr. Bell. "These animals must be fed."

Under the man's directions the boys tossed some meaty bones into the eagles' cage. The great birds tore the meat off hungrily. Then the Indians threw a hunk of raw meat to the bear, who woke up long enough to eat it. The fawns nibbled away at bunches of tender grass.

Some time later William found himself back on the towpath. The boats were moving slowly downstream, once again on their way to Albany. Mr. Bell and the Indian boys stood on the deck of the "Noah's Ark," waving good-by.

William sighed. The day of days was coming to an end, and he felt as if he had just returned from another world.

Suddenly a voice behind him said, "Where have you been? Mother is angry with you."

William turned to find Rome and Father standing behind him.

"Don't stretch the truth, Rome," Father said. "Mother's a little anxious, but she isn't angry. We wondered where you were, lad. You missed the music and the speeches. Aren't you hungry?"

William looked up at him. "I guess I am a little hungry, Father. I forgot all about the time, but I don't believe I missed a thing. I saw something I shall never forget as long as I live. I've been aboard the 'Noah's Ark.'"

Adventure at Home

THE WINTER of 1825-26 passed by. Another baby arrived in the Fargo family. She was a girl, and they named her Sarah Ann.

Now it was June. William had been out of school for nearly two months. He was eight years old now. The little one-room school house closed its doors as soon as spring and planting time arrived. The boys were needed at home in the fields.

Today William wiggled his toes in the damp dirt outside the front door. It felt cool and smooth. Yesterday had been Sunday. He had worn his shoes to the little church at Pompey.

He still remembered how those shoes squeezed his toes and hurt his feet.

Suddenly he heard the faint tinkle of a bell. He stopped wiggling his toes and listened.

There it came again. *Ting-a-ling! Ting-a-ling!*

Rome came running up the lane from the turnpike. "Come quick!" he shouted. "It's a red and yellow wagon."

William stared at him.

"Hurry!" Rome urged. "It will be gone if you don't hurry, all of you!"

Father looked at Mother. Neither of them seemed to be surprised, and William wondered how they could be so calm.

"It must be a peddler," Mother said.

Father nodded. "You carry Sarah Ann," he said. "I'll take Chan. We'll all go down the lane."

He scooped Chan up under one arm.

"Chan can walk," the three-year-old protested.

"I know you can," Father said with a laugh.

William and Rome started off at a run. This time William was in the lead. His feet fairly flew over the worn ruts in the lane. Behind him came Rome, then Father and Mother with the two little Fargos in the rear.

For a moment William's heart stood still. He could no longer hear the bell. Then he reached the end of the lane and understood why he heard nothing. A red and yellow wagon drawn by a small horse had stopped under a big elm tree by the side of the road. The driver was standing at the rear of the wagon, looking for something among the boxes and kegs inside.

As the Fargos approached, he turned around. He took off an old hat with a bright red feather in it and bowed low. His olive-brown skin was tanned by wind and weather. His black eyes sparkled beneath a head of curly black hair. In his ears he wore slender hoops of gold.

"You come to buy my goods?" he asked.

William swallowed hard. The man had an odd way of speaking and William could hardly understand him.

Father smiled. "We would like to look first," he said.

The man waved a hand toward his wagon. "To be sure, to be sure. You look all you want to. Thread, cloth, ribbons for your wife. Maybe a shaving mirror for you." He looked at the boys. "Something for the little ones, too."

He opened a heavy brown cardboard box. Inside were a dozen bone-handled pocketknives. They looked sturdy and strong.

The man lifted one from the box and opened the single blade. "See? The best steel. This is a Barlow knife. No better knife is made."

William and Rome stared at the knife. They knew they were too young to own knives, but there was no harm in wishing.

William walked around to the front of the peddler's wagon. Suddenly he gave a squeal that brought his brothers running.

"Rome! Chan! Come see what I found!"

The whole family hurried around to the front of the wagon. William was leaning over one wheel staring happily at something on the front seat. It was a strange, small creature like nothing the boys had ever seen before. It was dressed in a red and blue suit and had a small red cap on its head. Its little wrinkled face looked like an old man's. It beady black eyes darted from one Fargo to another as it held onto William's outstreached forefinger for dear life.

"He likes me!" William cried happily.

"What is it?" Rome asked in a puzzled voice. "It looks like a little old man."

Father laughed. "It's a monkey. I haven't seen one since I was a boy back in Connecticut."

The man beamed at the boys. "You like Jocko, eh? You like Jocko?"

"Yes!" the boys said together.

"Let him hold my finger, William," Rome begged. "He's held yours long enough."

William looked unhappy. "I found him."

Mother whispered to Father. He nodded his head and turned to the peddler.

"We'd like to invite you to dinner, Mr.———" he began.

"You may call me Alfredo," the peddler said with a smile. He turned to the monkey. "You hear that Jocko? The people invite us to dinner."

"We live up this lane," Father added.

The man nodded his head. "Yes. We will be happy to come."

Presently the red and yellow wagon was jogging up the lane to the Fargo farmhouse. William was still the happiest boy in the world. He sat on the seat beside Alfredo, and Jocko sat between them. Rome and Chan and Mother and Father with the two babies walked along behind.

The Barlow Knife

WILLIAM watched Alfredo as he leaned back in his chair. The Italian seemed contented. When the family had sat down at the table, there had been many things on it. There was golden-brown fried chicken. There was broiled ham. There was a dish of buttery mashed potatoes with a bowl of thick cream gravy beside it. There were green beans, plum preserves, and peach pickles. Last of all, there was a thick blueberry pie.

Alfredo patted his plump stomach. "That was the best dinner I have had since I left Italy," he said. "You cook like a queen, Mrs. Fargo."

He rose and pushed back his chair. "You come

56

see my wares now?" he asked. "I must be on my way soon."

William hurried out the door ahead of the family. He wanted to see those Barlow knives. He had thought of little else—except Jocko— since he had seen them.

The horse was still hitched to the wagon. It was standing at the end of the lane. As William walked toward it, a furry brown object streaked across the lane directly in front of the horse. Just behind it came the two dogs, Nip and Tuck, barking loudly. They had scared up a rabbit.

Frightened, the horse reared on its hind legs, then plunged forward.

"Stop!" Alfredo shouted from the porch.

William sprang for the reins, but he was too late. The horse was already galloping frantical- ly down the lane, with the wagon swaying wildly behind it. William knew that if it hit a tree it would be shattered to pieces.

He ran after the wagon as fast as he could go. As he ran he could hear Alfredo shouting loudly behind him.

The horse ran frantically toward the bend where the lane met the turnpike. Without a driver, the wagon could easily turn over there and scatter the peddler's wares far and wide.

However, William seemed to be gaining on the horse, and so did Alfredo behind him. By this time William was gasping for breath, but he ran even harder than ever.

In a few moments he was even with the driver's seat. Without a thought of his own safety, he gave a flying leap, caught the edge of the seat, and scrambled safely over the wheel.

He reached over the dashboard for the reins, which were dangling on the ground. When he gathered them in his hands, he did not pull them, for that would only frighten the horse more. However, the horse seemed to know that a driver

was in control once more. It slowed down a little and in another minute Alfredo jumped over the wheel on the other side. He took the reins from William's tight fingers.

"Whoa, there! Whoa! Slow down, there's a good fellow," he cried.

The horse slowly came to a standstill. It looked back meekly as if it had never run away in the first place.

The Fargos came running up.

"William, you might have been hurt—or killed!" Mother cried.

"You're a brave boy, William," Father said. His voice shook a little.

Alfredo patted William on the shoulder. "You saved my wagon," he said. "You saved my wares. How would Jocko and I earn a living if we did not have our wagon?"

"He kept his head when there was a need," Father said. "I'm proud of him."

"And I am grateful to him," Alfredo added. He took off his battered hat and bowed low to William. "Thank you, my young friend."

William turned red. He wished people would not make such a fuss. He had only done what seemed best at the time.

"All's well that ends well," Father said. "I'm glad our boy could help you, Alfredo."

By now all the Fargos were standing in a row, looking up at the peddler. He was on the seat of the wagon with the reins in his hands.

"I have business at Pompey that cannot wait," he said. "I must be on my way." Then he looked down at William. "Before I go, I want to give you something for all you have done."

A wild hope came into William's heart. His eyes went to Jocko, crouched on the seat beside his master. Alfredo saw the look.

"No, no, I cannot give Jocko away. Jocko—he is my friend," he said.

William swallowed. He understood. A man could not give away his friend.

The peddler turned and reached in the back of the wagon. He brought out a brown cardboard box and opened it. There lay the Barlow knives.

Alfredo counted them out carefully. "One for William. One for Rome." He hesitated, then smiled and took out another knife. "And one for little Chan, too."

"Chan is too little for a knife," Mother objected. "So are William and Rome."

"They will grow," Alfredo said. "Put the knives away until the boys are old enough."

Mother still hesitated.

"Any boy who is old enough to stop a runaway horse is old enough for a knife," Father said. He took the knife from the peddler and handed it to William. Then he handed the other two knives to Mother. "Keep these until you think Rome and Chan are old enough to have them."

William's eyes shone as he examined the new Barlow. He did not know another boy his age in the whole neighborhood who owned a knife.

Still Alfredo did not leave. He reached into a pocket and drew out a tiny golden heart on a fine gold chain.

"For Sarah Ann," he told Mother.

"Thank, you Alfredo," Mother said.

"Come again, Alfredo," Father told him.

"Thank you! Thank you, Alfredo!" the boys cried. "Good-by, Alfredo!"

The chorus of voices rang out after Alfredo as he clucked to the horses and the wagon rolled down the turnpike. *Clip-clop! Clip-clop!* went the horse's hoofs. *Ting-a-ling! Ting-a-ling!* went the little bell.

The Fargos watched the wagon until it was out of sight. Then they turned to go up the lane.

William looked a his new knife. "I'm glad I have it, but I'll never forget Jocko," he thought.

A Trip on a Canalboat

ONE DAY Mr. Fargo went to Buffalo to see his friend John Farley. Instead of riding his horse or taking a stagecoach, he went on a canalboat and took William with him. They sat on top of the boat's cabin, where they could watch the passing countryside.

William was much too excited to sit very still. Within a few minutes he had been all over the boat, from bow to stern. Now as he sat beside his father he was watching the four mules that pulled the boat. Each mule was hitched to a heavy rope that led back to the bow of the boat, and the mules walked in single file.

The last mule had a driver, a boy only a few years older than William. He wore tight-fitting trousers and a blue jacket, and he had a blue cap on his head that matched the jacket.

From his chair on the boat William stared at the driver. That was a fine-looking uniform, he thought. He wished that he had a uniform like it and could ride one of the mules and guide the boat on the path up the canal.

Suddenly the steersman in the stern of the boat blew a long blast on a horn. William jumped. The rider on the towpath turned his head.

"Low bridge! Everybody down!" he called.

"We don't need them both to tell us, do we?" William asked.

Father gave a chuckle. "I guess they want to be sure there are no bumped heads."

Now the boat was coming closer to the bridge. It seemed almost on a level with the upper deck.

"Duck!" Father warned.

William ducked. So did everyone else. In a little while the bridge was behind them.

"All clear!" the boy on the mule shouted.

The passengers raised their heads again. The driver sat straight in his saddle, with his eyes fastened on the towpath ahead. He was careful even if he was only a boy.

"Low bridge!" was called so many times that day that William grew tired of hearing the words. He would be glad when they reached Buffalo tomorrow afternoon.

Late in the afternoon the steersman suddenly began to sing.

> "I've got a mule, her name is Sal,
> Fifteen miles on the Erie Canal——"

The passengers, who were in a gay holiday mood, took up his words at once.

> "I've got a mule, her name is Sal,
> Fifteen miles on the Erie Canal."

The steersman grinned and winked at William.

By this time William was sitting at the rear of the cabin roof, with his legs dangling over the edge, where he could watch the steersman.

"She's a good old worker and a good old pal,
  Fifteen miles on the Erie Canal."

The people on board good-naturedly repeated his words.

"We've hauled some barges in our day,
  Filled with lumber, coal, and hay,
  And every inch of the way we know
  From Albany to Buffalo!"

The steersman finished in grand style and waved a hand for the passengers to join in the chorus. William sang with all his might.

"Low bridge, everybody down!
  Low bridge, for we're going through a town,
  And you'll always know your neighbor,
  You'll always know your pal,
  If you ever navigated on the Erie Canal."

William slid down from the roof to the main deck and landed on his bare feet. Father had said he could go without shoes until they reached Buffalo. The shoes were in Father's carpetbag in the cabin below.

"Hi, youngster," said the steersman. "Are you having a good time?"

"Yes, sir," William said politely. "I'm going to Buffalo with my father."

"Buffalo is a big town," the steersman replied. "You don't want to get lost there." Then, without giving William time to answer, he waved at the tiller. "Would you like to steer?"

William's eyes opened wide. "Do you think I could?" he said eagerly.

"Sure as anything," the man said. "Here. Hold tight to the tiller and keep it steady. Steady now. Keep her in the middle of the canal. Bear to the left when we come to the bend up there. Left— left. That's a good boy!"

William was panting slightly as the bank of the canal straightened out again. "Why did I have to steer the boat to the left? Wouldn't the mules have pulled it around the bend?"

"Her," the steersman corrected. "Always call a boat her."

"Her," William said. "Wouldn't the mules have pulled her around the bend anyway?"

"Of course, but this a big boat. She carries a heavy load for Sal and ——"

William's eyes twinkled. "Sal?"

The man nodded again, smiling. "Half the mules on this canal are named Sal. As I was saying, Sal and the other mules have a heavy load to pull, so I help them by making the boat follow as easily as possible."

William listened to every word. "I'd like to be a steersman on the canal," he said.

The man grunted. "It gets tiresome sometimes. Is this your first trip?"

"Yes, sir."

"I'll tell you what. We'll pass through a lock

about six o'clock. You will be below at supper. Keep your eye on the clock and come up on deck at six if you want to see a sight you won't forget for a while."

That evening William sat at the long supper table in the cabin with his father and the other passengers. The meal was good, but William thought Mother's cooking was better. He was about to take another bite of peach cobbler when he noticed that the clock on the wall said five minutes till six. He laid his spoon down.

"Will you excuse me, please?" he asked.

"Aren't you feeling well, son?"

"I feel fine," William said, "but it's almost time for——" The rest of his words were lost as he ran up the narrow stairs to the deck.

The steersman was still at the tiller. "You're in good time," he said.

"I didn't want to be late," William said.

"Boat ahoy!" someone shouted in the distance.

William looked ahead. Besides the towpath lay a little house. A man stood in front of the house, waving his hand at the approaching boat.

"That's the lockmaster," said the steersman. "We're about to enter the lock now."

William looked ahead with interest. The towpath and the boy and his mules had disappeared. In their place rose a high stone wall. A similar wall rose on the other side of the canal. The boat drifted to a stop between the walls. Then the

lockmaster closed the great wooden gates that stretched from one wall of the lock to the other. Other gates were already closed ahead of the boat.

"I feel shut in," William said.

The steersman laughed. "You are shut in. The canal on the other side of that lock ahead of us is higher than the part we have been traveling through. This lock will take us up to it just as if we were climbing up a step."

"I don't understand," William said.

"Look." The steersman pointed to water that poured through an opening in one wall ahead of the boat. "The lockmaster closes the gate behind us and lets water enter the lock through that opening. When the water in here is as high as the water on the far side of the lock ahead of us, the lockmaster will open the gate. Then we can travel on."

"My goodness!" William exclaimed and

studied the lock with interest. Presently he said, "What do people do when they get to Buffalo? Where do they all work?"

"Oh, they don't all stay in Buffalo," the steersman said. "Buffalo is just a jumping-off place for the West. People are swarming into Ohio, Indiana, Illinois, and up into Michigan Territory. Hundreds of them come across the Erie Canal from Albany every week."

"How do they travel when they leave the canal?" asked William.

"Some go in boats on the Great Lakes. Some travel in wagons or on horseback, and some even walk," the steersman replied.

William was silent a few moments, thinking. Then he said, "I wonder what it's like out there in the West. I wonder——"

Just then the captain of the boat came hurrying around the corner of the cabin. He was cross and worried.

"What's wrong?" the steersman asked.

"Young Johnny, the mule driver, is sick," the captain said. "He can't ride, and I must get this boat to Buffalo on time tomorrow."

The steersman scratched his head. "Can't one of the crew ride Sal?" he asked.

"You know Sal," the captain said, shaking his head. "She's a stubborn beast. She's used to a boy on her back and won't carry a pound more. And she won't budge unless someone rides her." His eyes fell on William standing near by. "Did you ever ride a mule, boy?"

"M-me?" William stuttered excitedly. "I've ridden mules, ponies, horses, everything with four legs. I even rode a cow once."

The captain turned to the steersman. "We should be in the next town in an hour and a half, and Johnny would have left us there anyhow. Another driver will be waiting for us there. This boy ought to do until then."

At that moment Father came up on deck.

William ran toward him. He was almost too excited to talk. "May I, Father? Please say yes! Wait till I tell people at home about this!"

"Wait! Wait! What's this about?" Father wanted to know.

When he understood why William was needed, he agreed for him to become a mule driver—for one hour and a half.

"Come along, boy," the captain said. "We've no time to lose."

William felt like a king as he threw one leg over Sal's back. As soon as she felt his weight, she started along the towpath, and the other mules followed after her.

William looked ahead into the darkening night. What was that in the distance? He stared hard, then smiled and looked back at the boat. Lights were shining in the cabin.

"Low bridge" he shouted. "Everybody down!"

Buffalo Boy

THE CANALBOAT had just docked at Buffalo. William was sorry to leave the friends he had made on the journey, but at the same time he was delighted by the sights and sounds of the city. Never before had he seen so many people, vehicles, and horses. There was so much noise and confusion that he almost wished for a moment that he were back in Pompey.

Then he saw a tall, tanned man striding toward the dock. "There's Uncle John!" he cried.

In a moment the two men were shaking hands. William stood waiting impatiently, first on one foot and then on the other.

At last Uncle John looked down at him. "Bless my soul!" he exclaimed. "You must have grown seven feet since I saw you last."

William grinned. He couldn't have like a real uncle more. Uncle John was actually just a good friend of the Fargo family.

"Let me have your luggage," Uncle John said, reaching for the carpetbag. "We must hurry. Aunt Jenny has supper ready, and the boys are expecting you."

As they walked along the streets William stared first on one side and then on the other. Big horses pulled heavily loaded wagons over the cobblestones. People hurried briskly here and there. William wondered where they were going.

"People seem to be in such a hurry," he said, thinking out loud.

Uncle John laughed. "They are in a hurry, boy. Buffalo is growing. There's not a town in the United States growing any faster. A lot of people pass through here on their way west—and many of them stay right here."

"I like it," William said. "It makes me feel so—so important. It makes me feel just as if I belong here."

Little wrinkles of amusement appeared at the corners of Uncle John's blue eyes.

"You do belong here. You're an American, aren't you? Well, this is America on the march."

William went on looking about him. There was so much to see and hear that his heart raced with excitement.

Just ahead of him a gaily painted wagon was drawn up to a street corner. It reminded William of Alfredo's wagon. It, too, was red and yellow, but it was open on all four sides and had a big sign at one end that read, "Watson's Medicine Show." Under the sign were rows and rows of bottles full of a ruby-colored liquid.

In the wagon a young man was playing a

guitar. Near him stood a tall thin man wearing a long black coat and a high beaver hat. He stood with one hand on the back of a chair and watched the crowd with half-closed eyes. When he looked at William, William felt uncomfortable.

The guitar player ended his concert with a catchy tune, and the people gathered on the sidewalk applauded. Then the thin man stepped forward and began to speak.

"La-adies and Gentlemen! I hope you have enjoyed my young friend with his guitar. And now to come to the more serious part of our program. Here is your opportunity to buy Morton's Golden Elixir. You will always be glad that you parted with a small sum of money to buy this great household remedy.

"This formula came to my grandfather from an old Indian chieftain in the North Woods. It may be used for cuts, bruises, insect bites, burns, pains, numbness, or any other disorder inside or out. In short, it is good for almost any ailment in man or beast."

He picked up a bottle and held it to the sun. All eyes were turned on him. Then he uncorked the bottle and sniffed at the contents. A smile spread over his face.

Meanwhile William's sharp eyes were roving over the crowd. He saw a youth hardly out of his teens slip quietly through the bystanders. He was so quiet and stealthy that people hardly knew he was there.

Suddenly the young man stumbled against an old farmer. "I beg your pardon," he said. At the same instant, he slipped one hand inside the farmer's greatcoat pocket. Quickly he drew out a wallet, then vanished into the crowd.

For a moment William could neither more nor speak. When he finally found his voice, he ran over to the farmer and seized his arm.

"Sir——" he began.

The old man turned.

"You've been robbed, sir!"

The old man turned pale. He felt in his pocket. "It's gone! My money's gone!" he cried.

William pointed in the direction the thief had taken. "He bumped into you just to steal your money. He was so quick I couldn't say anything."

The old man shook his head sadly. "I was going to buy winter supplies with that money."

Just then Uncle John and Father hurried up. "What's wrong here?" asked Uncle John.

"My pocket was picked," the farmer said.

William clenched his fists. "If only I'd been quicker! I didn't know what was happening."

"Robberies occur all the time in Buffalo," Uncle John said. "The town is full of thieves. I wish we could put them behind bars."

"I'd like to catch that thief!" William said hotly. "I'll know if I see him again, too. I'll never forget that face."

A Trip to
Niagara Falls

WILLIAM soon felt at home at Uncle John's house. Uncle John's wife seemed happy to see William and his father. Their seven children, all boys, were glad to see them, too.

"David, Joe, James, John, Robert, Silas, and Hiram," William recited as they sat around the supper table the first night. "Now I know all of you."

Four-year-old Joe stared solemnly at William. "There's just one of you for us to learn."

"There would be more if you came to our house," William told him. "I have two brothers and a little sister. Maybe you'll come someday."

Uncle John leaned back in his chair. "Well, it won't be tomorrow," he announced. "Tomorrow we're going to Niagara Falls."

The boys received the news with shouts of joy. William was glad, too. All his life he had heard about the Falls. Now he was really going to see them at last.

"We'll hitch up the team and pile into the wagon," Uncle John went on. "We'll have to leave before sunup in order to reach the Falls before dark. Then we'll spend the night with my brother Eph, who has a farm near by."

William began to count heads. "Will he have room for all of us?" he asked.

"Of course," said twelve-year-old Silas. "Some of us can sleep on the floor."

"Or in the barn," Hiram added.

"Or under the trees," said Robert. "I love to look up at the stars at night."

The next morning before the sun rose, William,

his father, and Uncle John's family were riding along a narrow country road toward Niagara Falls. Rolling meadows stretched away on either side of them. In the distance they could see another horse-drawn vehicle.

The morning passed quickly. Sometime after lunch William noticed a large river flowing beside the road.

"That's the Niagara River," John told him. "It doesn't look swift now, but just wait!"

The horses jogged along for several more hours. The Farleys were a happy family, and William wished that the rest of the Fargos were there.

Suddenly he pricked up his ears. There was a roaring sound in the distance that sounded like thunder. He looked puzzled. "It can't be thunder. There isn't a cloud in the sky."

The other boys laughed. "That's Niagara Falls," Robert told him. "You can hear the sound for mile around."

William could hardly believe him. Even though the sound grew louder with every turn of the wagon wheels, William could not understand how water falling over a ledge could make so much noise. It must take a lot of water to make that kind of roar.

At last the wagon reached a small settlement, and Uncle John reined the horses to a stop. "We're here," he announced. "Everybody out!"

The boys tumbled to the ground like young pupies. They rolled in the long grass. They wrestled with one another. They ran and jumped like puppies.

Presently William felt a hand on his shoulder. "Don't you want to see the Falls?" Father asked.

William sprang up. For a moment he had forgotten all about the Falls. He followed his father along a path and suddenly had his first glimpse of Niagara Falls.

A broad river swept forward to drop suddenly

over the edge of a sheer precipice. A cloud of mist rose from the gorge below, shutting part of the Falls off from view. Even though he stood at a safe distance from the Falls, William's face was damp from the spray. The roar of the falling water was deafening.

William went closer to the edge of the cliff and looked down. Far below the water swirled in whirlpools and eddies.

He drew a deep breath. "Goodness!" he whispered. "It—it does something to you!"

He felt his father's hand on his shoulder. "I've seen the Falls many times, William, but they still do something to me."

Finally Uncle John called everyone back to the wagon. "We must be going," he said. "We'll eat supper at the inn here. Then we'll push on to my brother's farm. We should be there by bedtime, I think."

Darkness had come by the time the travelers

reached the inn. Flares lighted up the yard. A crowd of fifty or sixty persons was gathered about a red and yellow wagon.

"It's the medicine show!" William exclaimed. "It's the one we saw yesterday in Buffalo."

"Let's hope the pickpocket didn't come along," Mr. Fargo said. He and Uncle John reached for their wallets and placed them inside their waistcoats where they would be safe.

"He is here!" William said, clutching his father's sleeve. "He's right there on the medicine show wagon."

Father and Uncle John looked where William was pointing. A slender young man climbed from the wagon and disappeared into the crowd. The two men exchanged glances.

"Could he be working with the show?" William wanted to know.

"We'll see," Uncle John replied. "Keep your eyes and ears open, boy."

William pushed his way through the crowd in search of the pickpocket.

Suddenly he caught his breath. Just ahead a prosperous-looking man and his wife were watching and listening to the guitar player as he played a tune. Near by was the pickpocket, making his way toward the couple.

Suddenly the pickpocket brushed against the other man. "I beg your pardon——" he began, and in the same instant William saw his hand slide into the other man's rear pocket.

William sprang forward and caught one of the pickpocket's legs with both arms. "Father!" he yelled at the top of his voice. "Uncle John!"

The pickpocket kicked and threshed about, trying to escape, but William hung on. The pickpocket swung at him with a clenched fist. At that moment Father rushed up and pinned the man's arms to his sides.

"Quick, John! Get a rope!" he shouted.

The pickpocket still struggled fiercely, but Father and William held on tight until Uncle John ran up with a rope.

By this time the crowd had forgotten the medicine show. Everyone gathered around Father and William and the pickpocket.

The young man was pale. "Why don't you go after him?" he demanded angrily, pointing toward the red and yellow wagon and its owner. "He's as guilty as I am."

People turned to look at the man in the long black coat and beaver hat, who was standing in the wagon. When a few people moved toward him, he suddenly whipped up the horses hitched to the wagon and galloped off. In a few moments the medicine show had disappeared.

Father turned to Uncle John. "Shall we go after him?" he asked.

Uncle John shrugged his shoulders. "Let him go. It's good riddance."

By now a man in hunting clothes and high black boots made his way through the crowd. "I'm the sheriff," he said. "What's going on?"

Uncle John told him the whole story. The sheriff turned to a companion. "Search him," he said, pointing to the prisoner.

The prisoner's pocket yielded a handful of small coins and a pigskin wallet.

The prosperous-looking man uttered an exclamation when he saw the wallet. He thrust his hand into his pocket and brought it out empty. "Why, that's my wallet!" he exclaimed. "There's a lot of money in it, too."

"You may thank this boy for its recovery," said Uncle John, pointing to William.

The stranger looked at William gratefully. "I shall do more than thank him."

William shook his head. "I don't want a reward," he said.

"Well, come along," Uncle John said. "We

must be on our way. If we don't get there soon
my brother Eph will think we have missed the
road to his farm."

"Not Eph Farley, by any chance?" the prosperous-looking man inquired.

Uncle John nodded. "Do you know him?"

The other man smiled. "His farm lies next to
mine. You may be sure I'll see this fine boy
again tomorrow."

He patted William on the shoulder. At the
same time the sheriff gave the prisoner a push.
"Get along with you," he ordered. "I'm taking
you back to Buffalo—and jail."

A Horse of
His Own

By the time Uncle John drove up to his brother's farmhouse, William was worn out. He tumbled out of the wagon with the other boys, feeling more dead than alive. He was already half asleep when a big man who looked like Uncle John came out of the house to meet them. With the other boys, William stumbled up a narrow stairway to the second floor. There he fell into a high four-poster bed and was asleep at once.

The sun was streaming in through the windows when he awoke. He blinked his eyes for a moment. Then he remembered where he was.

"William!" Uncle John called.

93

"Yes, sir," William answered. He jumped out of bed and hurried into his clothes. Then he hurried downstairs.

Father, Uncle John, and the boys were already eating breakfast. The man William had seen last night was sitting at the head of the table. He and Uncle John were as alike as two peas. William knew he must be Uncle John's brother. Beyond in the kitchen a motherly-looking woman bustled about getting breakfast.

Father smiled at William. "I thought you were going to sleep all day."

William grinned sheepishly. "I guess I would have if Uncle John hadn't called me."

Uncle John's brother pulled out a chair. "Sit down and have same breakfast."

William slipped into the place beside him. "Thank you, sir. I guess I am hungry, Mr.——"

"You may call me Uncle Eph," the man said. "After all, I'm as much your uncle as Uncle John

94

is. Would you like ham or oatmeal first this morning, William?"

William held out his plate. "Ham, please, Uncle Eph," he said.

Uncle Eph put a juicy slice of broiled ham on the boy's plate. Then he added a mound of scrambled eggs. "That should be a start for a growing boy. I'm proud to claim you for a nephew, William. A boy who can capture a thief almost single-handed is worth claiming."

William blushed. "I didn't do anything much, Uncle Eph," he said.

Uncle Eph looked at him over his spectacles. "That's not the way my friend John Taylor feels about it."

"John Taylor?"

"He's the man whose wallet was stolen. If you hadn't seen the thief and held on to him until help came, Mr. Taylor would have lost almost five hundred dollars."

William's eyes flew open. So did the other boys'. "That's a lot of money," William said.

"Mr. Taylor was waiting for me this morning when I went out to milk the cows," Uncle Eph went on. "He wants your father to bring you over to his farm after breakfast."

"Whatever for?" William asked. "I don't want a reward for helping get his money back."

Uncle Eph smiled. "I think you had better go," he said. "Mr. Taylor is expecting you."

When breakfast was over, William and his father left for Mr. Taylor's farm.

"Aren't the other boys coming?" William asked.

His father shook his head. "They're going to walk over the farm with Eph and John. Just you and I are going."

The ride to the Taylors' house was short but pleasant. It was autumn now, and the fields were ripe with grain. As William and his father neared the Taylors' gate, William saw a number of horses grazing in a large meadow. Some were standing still. Others were galloping the length of the field. They were a beautiful sight.

William sighed. "I certainly wish I had a horse," he said.

Father gave an odd little laugh, and William looked at him in surprise. What was so funny about that remark?

In a few minutes William and his father were inside Mr. Taylor's house. William looked about with interest. Some huge deer antlers hung over the fireplace. An Indian headdress hung on the wall near by. Near that were some Indian beads dangling from a hook. On the other side of the fireplace was a framed letter. William went over to read it, but it was written in a language he did not know. He wondered what the letter said.

At that moment his father's voice called him back to the room. "Mr. Taylor is talking to you, William," he said.

William turned. "I was trying to read the letter," he said.

Mr. Taylor smiled. "I don't suppose you know Spanish, young man?"

"No, sir."

"Well, neither did I when I was your age. I learned it later when I did some surveying in the West."

"Have you been in the West, sir?" William asked. "The real West?"

Both men laughed at his eagerness. "Some people think western New York is in the West," Mr. Taylor said.

"Oh, I mean way out there," William explained. "Beyond the jumping-off place."

"Where did you get those words?"

"From the steersman on the canalboat," William said. "He said that Buffalo is just the jumping-off place for the West."

"He was right," Mr. Taylor agreed. "I've been

in the real West. There are miles and miles of flat country with nothing but grass in sight. And beyond that are mountains that seem to rise halfway to the sky. It's a great place, William Fargo. It gives a man room to grow."

"I think I'd like to see the West," William said thoughtfully.

"Keep that idea in mind," Mr. Taylor told him. "I may go back someday myself. Then again I may stay here. The West is for the young, strong, and daring. And I'm not young any more."

"Oh, come now!" protested Father. "You're not old, either."

John Taylor chuckled. "Well, I may go back, but I have other business this morning. Bring William out to the barn, Mr. Fargo. I have something to show him."

In a few moments William was sitting on the top rail of the fence at one end of a big white barn. His father leaned against the fence at his

side. The two of them were waiting for Mr. Taylor to come from the barn.

Presently he came through the wide doors, leading a young mare at the end of a halter.

William's eyes opened wide at sight of the horse. She was beautiful. Sunlight gleamed on her golden-brown coat. When she saw William and his father, she held her head high and pranced a little on slender legs.

William caught his breath. "What a treasure!" he exclaimed.

Mr. Taylor patted her. "Steady there, girl, steady now." He turned to William. "Do you like her, boy?"

"Like her! She's the most beautiful horse I've ever seen!" William cried.

Mr. Taylor handed him the halter. "Well, then, she's all yours."

For a moment William was speechless. Then he recovered, "Oh, but I couldn't take her! Father wouldn't let——" He turned to his father. "That is—would you, Father?"

Before Mr. Fargo could reply, Mr. Taylor offered William the halter again. "She's saddle-broken, but she's still a little skittish. She needs a bit of training yet. I think you're just the lad to finish the job."

William clutched the halter in his hand. With a question in his eyes, he turned to look at his father.

"Thank Mr. Taylor, son," Mr. Fargo said. "That's a wonderful gift."

Suddenly words began to tumble from William's lips. "I can't believe it! Mr. Taylor, I'll never forget you as long as I live! I'm the luckiest boy in the whole world. Thank you, sir! Thank you, thank you! I can't imagine why you gave her to me."

Mr. Taylor looked almost as happy as William. "Let's just say that I know a good boy and a good horse when I see them. What are you going to name her?"

William turned back to the mare and ran a loving hand over her smooth flanks.

"Haven't you already named her?" he asked.

Mr. Taylor's eyes twinkled. "It seems to me a boy should name his own horse."

William thought for a moment. He turned puzzled eyes to his father. "I can't think of any name good enough for her."

Mr. Fargo smiled. "What did you call her when she came out of the barn?"

William frowned. "I don't know. Yes, I do, too. I said, 'What a treasure!' That's it! I'll name her Treasure and call her Trez for short." He laid his curly head against the mare's sleek neck. She turned her head and looked at him. "That's it," he said again. "My Treasure."

The two men laughed. "It looks like love at first sight," Father said.

A small frown appeared on William's forehead. "How will we get her home? They won't take her on a canalboat, will they?"

"Of course," Mr. Taylor told him. "Some canalboats carry freight as well as passengers."

"I'm going to stay right with her," William declared. "I won't leave her for one minute. I'll sleep with her and exercise her when the boat stop long enough."

"And eat with her?" Father asked. "I can see you sharing a measure of oats with her."

William grinned. "Well, maybe I won't do that. But there's nothing to stop me from carrying my meals down and eating with her."

Chased by Wolves

It was a cold threatening day. The overhanging gray clouds promised more snow. Already it was several inches deeper than usual for North Falls, where William was spending the winter.

"I'm glad you're here," said Mr. Jackson. "If this snow continues, it will take both of us to keep open the paths to the barn and the other farm buildings."

"And a path to the well," William added.

"And the well," Mr. Jackson agreed. "Of course, we could melt snow for ourselves, but the animals need water, too."

William blew on his hands and rubbed them

briskly together. His cheeks were rosy from the nipping winter air.

"Do you suppose it's this cold at Pompey?" he said. "I hope not."

"It's cold all over the state," Mr. Jackson replied. "It's as cold a winter as I've ever seen, and I've seen a lot of them."

William did a little jig to warm his feet. He would be glad when the chores were finished and he could return to the cabin. It would be pleasant to thaw out by the big open fire. First, however, the cows and horses must be fed.

William poured a big measure of oats for Trez. "Eat them all, girl," he said. "They'll help to keep you warm."

Trez whinnied as if she understood him. In William's mind there was no doubt that she understood every word he said. He wouldn't have been greatly surprised if she had answered him. She was the smartest horse he knew.

106

When he and old Mr. Jackson had finished their chores they returned to the cabin. William sat before the fire, while Mr. Jackson placed big bowls of hot rabbit stew on the table.

"It was a lucky day for me when I hired you to spend the winter with me," the old man said.

William shook his head. "I'm the lucky one. I had had just about all the school I could get, and there's not much to do at Pompey during the winter months. I'm glad you asked me to come up here and help you with your trapping."

Mr. Jackson glanced toward the pile of otter and marten skins in the far corner of the cabin. "You've been a real help," he said. "I'm not so spry as I once was. You've saved me a lot of walking, and I already have more skins than usual at this time of the year."

William looked at the skins, too.

"How old are you?" the old man asked.

"I'll be thirteen next May," William replied.

"You look older," Mr. Jackson said. "You're tall and strong. And you use your head for something besides your hat. You think before you act. How would you like to be my partner in my trapping business? I'm not getting any younger, and I could use a young fellow like you."

William's face lighted up. "Thank you, Mr. Jackson. It's nice of you to want me."

"Then you will?"

William shook his head. "No sir. I'm not sure what I want to do, but it isn't trapping. I like to be around people too much to stay a trapper all my life. And frankly, sir, I want to make a lot of money someday."

"Don't we all?" the old man said.

"I'm serious," William said. "We're never hungry or cold at home, but we don't have much. I'd like to see my parents take things easier. I have several brothers and sisters, too, and I'd like to see them have a chance in the world."

108

Mr. Jackson dipped a gourd into the wooden water bucket and took a long drink. "You're a good boy, William. I hope you get your wish, but I want you to remember that the offer is still open. Meanwhile, I have an errand for you to do tomorrow morning."

William nodded. "Yes, sir."

"I've sold a gun to Jim Fisher, who lives about fourteen miles north of here. I promised I would deliver it tomorrow. Will you take it for me?"

"Why, of course," William answered.

"I'd like to go along," Mr. Jackson said. "It's a pleasant ride and a fairly good road, but this cold weather makes my old bones ache. I think I'd better stay at home by the fire. You and Trez ought to enjoy the sleigh ride, though."

William's eyes danced. "May I take the sleigh?"

"Yes, the snow is deep enough now, and packed."

The next morning William was ready early. He

was eager to be off. The snow clouds were still hanging low in the sky, but the sun was trying to shine. In spite of that, the air was colder than ever this morning.

Trez was hitched to the slender sleigh, which was black with bright red trimmings. William was bundled up so that only his eyes and nose could be seen. The bells on the mare's harness jingled as she turned her head.

Mr. Jackson looked up at the sky. "I don't know whether I should let you go or not," he said. "It looks as if we may get more snow."

William gathered up the reins. The gun lay on the seat beside him. "Trez and I like snow."

The old man frowned. "I wouldn't want you to get caught in a blizzard."

"I'll be back before dark," William assured him. "Now I'd better get started, Mr. Jackson. It's a long way to Mr. Fisher's place."

"I wish I hadn't promised Jim the gun today,"

110

the old man said. "If it weren't for that, I'd just let him wait."

William shook the reins over Trez's head. He smiled. "We'll make it all right," he said. "Don't worry, Mr. Jackson."

Mr. Jackson watched the sleigh glide gracefully away. Trez was stepping high and shaking her head proudly. The sleigh bells jingled in the cold air. William sat up straight.

The old man chuckled, then turned back to the cabin. He was glad he could sit by the fire.

Meanwhile William rode along in the sleigh behind the golden-brown mare. Both boy and horse were in high spirits. They made such good time that the sun was still overhead when William drew up at Jim Fisher's cabin.

Mr. Fisher came out to meet him. "I wasn't looking for you today," he said. "The weather looks pretty threatening."

William looked up at the sky. The sun was no

longer visible. The clouds hung lower. A sharp wind was coming out of the east.

William shivered. "Br-r-r! I believe you're right, Mr. Fisher."

"Come inside and warm yourself," Fisher urged. "You must be chilled to the bone."

William stayed longer at Mr. Fisher's than he intended. His host insisted that he sit down to a bowl of steaming hot soup. It tasted good after the long drive, and he let Mr. Fisher persuade him to have another one. Then he went out to the woodlot with Mr. Fisher to look at a new trap.

At last William made ready for the ride home. Mr. Fisher counted out a handful of coins and wrapped them in a piece of paper. "Here's the money," he said.

William handed him a piece of folded paper in return. "And here's a receipt," he said.

"Your word's good enough," Fisher said.

William grinned. "That's not good business. You'd better keep the receipt. Mr. Jackson gave it to me before I left this morning. He'd never forgive me if I came back with it."

"All right!" Jim Fisher laughed. "Sure you won't spend the night?"

William shook his head. "Mr. Jackson would worry if I didn't come home. I told him I'd be back. Besides, I'm his messenger." He threw

back his head and spoke in mock tones. " 'Neither snow, nor rain, nor heat, nor darkness, are permitted to obstruct their speed.' "

"Where did you hear that?" Fisher asked.

"From a teacher we had at Pompey last year," William said. "It comes from an old Greek book he carried around with him. That man wasn't a very good teacher, but he loved to read."

"Well, you'd better be on your way unless you want the snow to obstruct your speed," Jim Fisher said. "It must be two o'clock."

"Two!" William whistled in dismay. "I'll never make it home before dark. I didn't know so much time had passed."

"I'm afraid you won't," Fisher agreed. "Tell Jackson I'm much obliged for the rifle. And wait——" He hurried inside and came back with something wrapped in coarse sacking, which he threw in the bottom of the sleigh. "Here's some fresh venison for you. I killed a deer yesterday."

William waved his hand in farewell and cried "Giddap!" to Trez. The sleigh moved smoothly away into the forest.

The first part of the journey homeward was uneventful. William kept looking at the sky overhead. The sun dropped toward the horizon.

"It must have taken me five hours to come," he thought. "The earliest I can hope to get home is seven. It will be dark long before then."

It was almost dusk when the snow began to fall. By then the east wind was sharper than ever. The snow added to the growing darkness, and Trez began to pick her way uncertainly. Soon the snow was coming down so hard that William could see only a short distance ahead.

"Don't leave the road, Trez," he pleaded. "This is a cold night to be lost."

The mare laid back her ears and pushed on into the night. She seemed as anxious to get home as William was.

Suddenly she stumbled. The sleigh lurched. William pulled it back to level ground. Then he noticed that Trez was limping. He stopped her and climbed out to see what was wrong. There was a bad cut on her right foreleg where she had stumbled against a stone.

William patted her quivering flanks. "Bad luck, girl," he said softly. "We'll just have to go slow, even if we don't get home until midnight. I'd turn back to Mr. Fisher's place, but I think we're more than halfway home."

They jogged on for about half an hour. Trez limped painfully. It tore at William's heart to force her on, but going on was better than remaining out in the night.

Suddenly he sat up with a start. A long, weird sound came out of the darkness.

Owr-r-r-r!

William had never heard the sound before, but he knew instantly what it was. Timber wolves!

116

For a second he hoped he had dreamed it. Then it came again.

Owr-r-r!

William shivered. He remembered stories he had heard about timber wolves. They could smell the scent of blood for miles and come in a straight course to find it. He thought of the cut on Trez's foreleg. It was not bleeding much because of the cold, and he had thought he could get home without trouble. Now——

He shivered again.

Then he noticed the sack of venison on the floor of the sleigh. "Maybe it's the venison the wolves smell," he thought, but he knew that it was not. The merciless beasts were after his beautiful Trez. Why, oh, why had she stumbled over that stone?

Owr-r-r-r! R-r-r-r-r!

The sounds were closer now. The pack was gaining on him, though it was still several miles away. He drew the whip from its socket on the sleigh. Never once in the three years he had owned Trez had he used a whip or spur on her. Must he do it now? He gave her a sharp flick. She bolted with fright and surprise, and seemed to limp worse than ever. William groaned and put the whip back in its place. He could not use it on her again, come what may.

Half-standing in the sleigh, he urged her on as if she were human. This plan worked better. In spite of her injury, she trotted faster. Maybe they could reach home and safety yet. William shook the reins. "Come on, girl!" he cried.

Again the chilling howls came through the cold night air. William glanced over his shoulder. Over the brow of the hill came five gray shapes galloping through the darkness.

"Go, girl, go!" he pleaded.

The wolves came closer and closer. They were gaining steadily, as they might in a bad dream.

118

William picked up the whip again, then put it back. Trez could go no faster.

Through the darkness and the falling snow William could see the gray forms running just behind the sleigh now. Soon they would be even with it. Then they would reach Trez. They would spring at her and tear her to pieces. He would be next.

A sudden thought struck him. Holding the reins firmly in one hand, he reached down for a hunk of venison. He hurled it behind him. For a moment the flying forms stopped. He could hear their snarls as they fought over the meat.

At least the venison delayed them for a moment, and every moment counted in this wild race. Three more times he threw the venison to them. Then it was gone. If only he had the rifle he had delivered to Mr. Fisher!

At last the snarling beasts reached the sleigh. William could almost feel their hot breath. He

could see their red tongues hanging out of their mouths and their white fangs gleaming in the darkness. A cold chill ran down his spine.

Suddenly he struck out with his whip, lashing the leader across the face. The whip drew blood, and the wolf howled with pain.

In an instant the other four were upon him. William shuddered as he heard the savage sounds that came from their throats.

"Faster, Trez!" he cried.

In too short a time the remaining beasts came alongside the sleigh again. William's hands were shaking as he reached for the whip.

His blow was sure. Another wolf was down. The sleigh sped on through the night.

Twice more William struck at his foes. Each time there was one less wolf in the pack.

At last only the fiercest wolf remained. William struck at it with the whip in vain. It leaped to one side and kept on until it finally reached the front of the sleigh. A few more feet and it would spring at Trez. William reached forward with the whip. He missed again.

Suddenly a light shone in the distance. At the side of the road William saw the broken-down wagon that lay near Mr. Jackson's cabin. Safety at last—but could Trez make it?

Now the wolf was running even with her.

William rose to his feet and shouted with all his might. "Help! Help! Mr. Jackson!"

The door of the cabin burst open. Mr. Jackson ran out, his rifle in his hands. When he saw the wolf he raised the rifle quickly to his shoulder. In the same instant the wolf leaped.

Bang!

The wolf fell to the ground and thrashed about for a few moments. Then it lay still.

William stopped Trez and sprang from the sleigh. He ran to the mare and threw his arms about her neck.

His voice was shaking. "Oh, Trez! You're safe! You're safe!"

"And so you are," Mr. Jackson said thankfully as he ran forward.

William turned. "Well, yes, I guess I am," he said, as if surprised. "Believe me, Mr. Jackson, this is one night I'll never forget!"

The Mail Route

IT WAS an exciting day for the Fargos. They were all gathered outside the house to see William ride away.

Mother sighed. "Just think! We have a son old enough to have a real job."

"A job with the United States government at that," Father added.

Rome grinned at seven-year-old Chan. He spoke so softly that Mother could not hear him. "That was quite a breakfast. I wish we had one like it every day. Can't you arrange to go to work so Mother will cook another one like it?"

Chan sniffed. "You'd think William was leaving forever instead of riding a mail circuit twice a week."

"Better not tell Mother that," Rome said.

At that moment Trez came around the corner of the house with William on her back. For a thirteen-year-old boy he sat tall in the saddle. He and the horse made a striking picture. The golden-brown mare was even more beautiful than she had been four years ago when she was a present to the eldest Fargo boy.

From the very beginning William had ridden her with grace and skill. He, too, had grown since he had acquired her. Today, as he smiled down at his family, he seemed to be almost a part of the horse he rode.

Now he gathered the reins in his hands and waved. "Good-by! I'll see you all tomorrow night," he said.

Trez cantered away. The rest of the family watched until he and his horse reached the gate and turned onto the Great Western Turnpike. Then one by one they scattered to do their morning chores. William might be going away for the first time, but there was still work to be done.

Meanwhile William rode along in the bright sunshine until he reached the farmhouse of the man for whom he was working. This man held a contract to deliver the United States mail in his part of New York State.

William had scarcely drawn rein in front of the house when Mr. Dan came out to meet him. He was carrying two new saddlebags. They were shiny and new and smelled as only good leather can. They were stuffed with newspapers, small packages, and sealed letters.

"You're a half hour earlier than I expected you to be," Mr. Dan said approvingly. "At this rate you'll make a good mail carrier."

William reached down for the saddlebags. "I hope you're right," he said cheerfully. "I want to be a good carrier. I want to be good at everything I do."

He turned to arrange the saddlebags behind him. Mr. Dan watched him as he worked with a little smile of approval. It was clear William knew how to arrange the weight of the bags so that they would not rub Trez.

"William Fargo, you have a big job to do," Mr. Dan said at last. "This is the United States mail. The post office department is the newest addition to President Jackson's cabinet. The department must pay for itself. Don't forget to collect delivery fees. The government at Washington expects me to account for every penny people owe for the delivery of mail. It expects me to account for every penny I collect."

William held out a little black book which he had taken from his pocket. "I'll enter every fee in this," he said.

"Good! That's good business," Mr. Dan said.

"Be careful now, William. Ride carefully, and don't let anyone take advantage of you. I'll see you tomorrow night."

When William reached the turnpike again, he turned north toward Manlius, a town of some size near Syracuse.

"All right now, Trez," he said, slapping her gently with the reins. "Let's go to work. We ought to reach Manlius by noon."

About mid-morning he reached his first stop. A small crowd stood near the building that was both tavern and country store. The crowd had gathered to watch the mail rider arrive. The arrival of the mail was a big event in a little place like Watervale.

William slid from the saddle. He felt rather important as he unlocked one saddlebag and took out the mail for Watervale.

A tall, handsome man with folded arms stood on the tavern porch and watched him. The man was better dressed than others in the crowd, but a black patch over one eye gave him an almost sinister look. He watched William with a sneering smile that William did not like.

As William went up the steps with the mail, the man looked him up and down. Then he turned to the nearest bystanders.

"The government seems to be choosing children as post riders nowadays," he said.

Rude laughter went up from the crowd. William's face turned red, but he made no reply.

Inside the building, the owner of the store and tavern looked up as William laid a pile of letters and papers on the counter. A hearty smile came over the man's face.

"You must be William Fargo," he said.

William nodded. He was still too angry to speak calmly.

The storekeeper looked out the door. "I heard it all," he said quietly. "You mustn't mind Jean

Roddy. Nobody who is anybody thinks much of him. He comes from a good family, but he is a worthless, good-for-nothing scamp."

William felt his good spirits coming back. This man was understanding and kind.

The storekeeper put out a hand for William to shake. William liked his firm handclasp.

"My name is Ira Curtis," the man said. "I'm glad to know you."

"I'm William George Fargo," William said. "Maybe I'm young, but I was hired to do the job, and I'm going to do it."

Mr. Curtis held him off at arm's length and looked him over. Then his eyes began to twinkle.

"I think you'll get it done," he said. "You don't look like the sort of person who would give up easily."

William laughed. "You make a fellow feel mighty good. That man out yonder makes him feel just the opposite."

Mr. Curtis shrugged his shoulders. "I always say there are two kinds of people." He began to sort the mail. William opened his little black book and studied it.

"That will be a dollar and sixteen cents, sir," he said.

The storekeeper looked at him with approval. "So you're a good businessman, too."

He opened the cash drawer and counted out the money. William slipped the coins into the stout mail bag and turned to go.

"Wait a minute," Mr. Curtis said. "Aren't you going to stay for dinner? We set the best table this side of Syracuse."

William hesitated. "I thought I'd eat at Manlius," he said.

Ira Curtis gave a snort. "There's not a place in Manlius to compare with mine. What time did you eat breakfast, young fellow?"

"Six o'clock," William confessed. His stomach

was beginning to tell him that it was time for dinner. "I could eat."

"It's eleven o'clock now." Mr. Curtis turned and called through an open door. "We have a special guest today, Mother. The new mail carrier is here. Is dinner ready?"

In a short time William found himself across the table from Mr. Curtis and his wife. They were having an early meal before they opened the doors to the public.

The dining room was spotless. The scrubbed pine floor was as clean as the table. Checked curtains hung at the windows. A gay bouquet of flowers was in the center of the table.

And the food! William did not believe that even Mother could have prepared it better. Chicken and dumplings, creamy turnips, well-seasoned potatoes, spicy pickles, brown crusty bread with crabapple jelly to spread on it—it was all delicious, he thought. Last of all came a light,

wonderful blackberry cobbler. William thought that was the best of all.

As he ate, William thought of the long ride ahead of him. He was sure that he would travel better on a full stomach.

At last he rose to his feet. "I must be going, but I won't forget this delicious dinner," he said. "It was wonderful."

Mrs. Curtis beamed at him. "There will be another one waiting for you when you come by at the end of the week."

As William left the tavern and walked toward his horse, he saw the man named Jean Roddy again. He was mounting a big black horse that would have made almost two of Trez.

Roddy wheeled the animal about sharply, brushing against William as he did so. He gave William a nasty look, but William was so relaxed after his good dinner that he paid no attention.

"Get up, Lucifer!" Roddy shouted.

The man and horse went up the road in a cloud of dust. William was glad that he would be going in the other direction.

Soon William himself was on his way again. The miles passed steadily as he jogged along. At Manlius he delivered the mail, collected his fees, and turned south again. Oran was the next stop, then Delphi. By evening he reached Fabius, where he spent the night in a plain but decent inn. He had covered more than half of the forty-mile circuit he was supposed to ride.

The next morning he started out early. One more stop at Apulia and then he would be ready for the trip home. This job would not always take even two whole days.

Quite a while later William came to the top of the high hill that overlooked his home. He looked down at the farmhouse below him in the valley and burst into a merry whistle. Three long days lay before him now before he had to start out on his mail route again—three days in which he could help around home or do whatever he wished.

He liked being a mail carrier. Carrying the mail not only enabled him to earn money—it enabled him to see new scenes and faces, and it presented him with a task worth doing.

"I'm a lucky boy," he told a squirrel running across the road. "I'm a really lucky boy!" With that, he slapped Trez with the reins and started downhill toward home.

The Mail Must Go Through

"WILLIAM Fargo may be only sixteen, but he has been carrying the mail for three years. I'd trust him with anything I have," Mr. Dan told his wife one morning.

"Even with this?" She picked up a package from the top of the open mail pouch. He eyes were as troubled as her voice.

"Even with that," said her husband firmly. "Let me read that letter again."

He picked up the letter from Albany. It had come in the mail which Mr. Dan was about to hand over to young William.

The letter read:

Dear Dan:

I am sending by post a packet containing several hundred dollars. It is addressed to my father, Micah Dawes, who lives on a small farm between Manlius and Fabius. You may think I should send it directly to a bank at Manlius. Well, you don't know my father. He has made up his mind that he wants it right in his own hands. Will you please instruct the post rider to place it there?

With best regards,
John M. Dawes

There was a quick step on the porch. In a moment William Fargo entered the door. He had come to pick up the mail pouches.

He had grown in the last few years. Now he was as tall and almost as heavy as a man.

Mr. Dan handed the pouches to William. "I want you to be especially careful of them this time, William," he said. He told about the letter he had received and the packet of money. William listened carefully. He nodded as he shouldered the pouches.

138

"You may depend on me, sir," he promised.

"I'll do my very best to see that the money reaches Mr. Dawes."

"I know that, William," Mr. Dan said, clapping him on the shoulder.

As usual, William's first stop was at Watervale. As he fastened Trez to the hitching rail, William saw Lucifer, Jean Roddy's big black stallion, several places down the line. He frowned. Time had not lessened his dislike of the man or of his horse. He wondered if Lucifer was really faster than Trez. Roddy was always boasting that he was.

"I don't care whether Lucifer can outrun Trez or not," William muttered. "I still have the best horse in New York State."

By now he was inside the general store. Ira Curtis and his wife were working as usual. Each looked up and gave William a smile. In the three years they had known him, they had come to think of him almost as a son. They never had had a son of their own.

"Good morning to my favorite people!" William said as he entered the store.

Mr. Curtis laughed. "Get along with you, boy. You have Welsh blood in you, not Irish. Save that flattery for those who believe it."

William grinned. "Maybe I have some Irish blood in me, too. It's not flattery, either. I have lots of favorite people. I didn't say you were the only ones."

Mr. Curtis smiled at his wife. They knew how popular William was on every mile of his route. Because they were fond of him, the knowledge made them happy. Mr. Curtis did not intend to show his feelings, however.

"You're impossible!" he growled. "I wonder that you hold your job."

"Is that so?" William demanded. He turned a wooden chair around and seated himself astride it. He folded his arms across the back of the chair. "Would you like to know what I'm carrying today?"

He told them about the money in the locked mail pouch on its way to old Micah Dawes. He was so eager to tell his story that he missed the anxious look that passed between Mr. and Mrs. Curtis. His words tumbled out rapidly one after the other.

"I don't like it," Mrs. Curtis said when he had finished.

"Why not?" William asked in surprise.

"It's dangerous," she said.

"Dangerous! What's dangerous about it?" William wanted to know.

Mr. Curtis nodded his head. "She's right, my boy. It is dangerous."

William turned from one to the other. He could hardly believe his ears. He had never thought of danger before.

Mr. Curtis was talking now. "There's a long lonely stretch between Manlius and Fabius. After all, Oran and Delphi are only wide spots in the road. There was a hold-up only a few miles from Fabius last week. Haven't you heard about it?"

William shook his head.

"I know you've been delivering mail for quite a while," Mr. Curtis went on. "However, I doubt if you've ever carried any large sums of money in those mail pouches. Folks just don't send money that way—at least not in western New York. It isn't safe."

"It should be," William insisted. "The postal service is a part of the United States government. That should make it safe."

"Perhaps it should." Mr. Curtis sighed. "Perhaps someday the postal service will be perfectly safe. Right now there are still bandits."

He went to a drawer behind the counter and took out a leather belt and holster. In the holster was a big, shiny revolver. Williams' eyes lighted with excitement when he saw it.

"Have you ever fired a revolver, William?" Mr. Curtis asked.

William nodded. "Father has a pistol like that. We boys have practiced with it some."

Mr. Curtis handed the weapon to the boy. "Then take it with you. You may need it."

William smiled. "Thanks, Mr. Curtis. I don't think I'll need it at all, but I'd like to carry it just once."

He was strapping the belt around his waist when he heard an odd noise outside. It sounded as if someone trying to walk quietly had stepped on a twig. Both William and Mr. Curtis looked up, and Mr. Curtis hurried to the window. He thrust his head out, then turned back with a worried frown.

"I would have sworn I heard footsteps outside," he said. "Did you?"

"I don't know. I heard something, but I don't know what it was."

William looked at himself in the long mirror at the end of the room. The holster and pistol made him look quite manly and capable of taking care of himself, he thought.

Mrs. Curtis thought otherwise. "I just know you'll go and get hurt, William Fargo," she said. "I just know it!"

"The idea is to hurt someone else," he husband said drily.

William put one arm around Mrs. Curtis. "No one is going to get hurt," he said. "All I'll see between Manlius and Mr. Dawes's farm will be a few rabbits and chipmunks. I'll be back here safe and sound at the end of the week." He patted her shoulder. "Don't you worry about me. I'll be all right."

William climbed into the saddle and turned Trez toward Manlius. He really did not feel so sure about the matter, but he did not want the Curtises to know that. As he rode away from Watervale, he thought of the noise outside the window. Could anyone have heard him telling about the money he was taking to Mr. Dawes?

Presently he came to a little clump of trees at the side of the road. He dismounted and opened one of the saddle bags. There on top lay the packet, wrapped in heavy paper.

William looked up and down the road. No one was in sight. He thrust the packet deep into an inner pocket of his coat. Then he closed the saddle bag and locked it again. A few moments later he was riding along once more.

At Manlius he delivered the mail at the little post office. The postmaster, a middle-aged man who was new at the job, looked at William over his spectacles.

"You're pretty young to be carrying the mail, aren't you?" he asked.

By now William was tired of hearing people talk so much about his age. "I'm getting older every day," he said quietly. "I dont mean to boast, but I haven't heard any complaints."

"Humph!" was the postmaster's only comment.

William temper flared, but he said nothing. He had learned to keep still. There was a time when he would have answered, but he had learned that such answers gained nothing.

However, he did not cool off until he was riding away from Manlius. Then he began to think about the money again. He had several hours of riding ahead of him yet—first to Delphi and then to Oran. Then he could deliver the packet to Mr. Dawes and ride on to Fabius, where he would spend the night. He would breathe much easier after he left the money with Mr. Dawes.

Nothing happened on the first stage of the journey. At Delphi the postmaster came out to meet him.

"Thought maybe the bandit had you," he said. "There's one around, you know."

William shook his head. "Not yet."

"Well, be careful," the postmaster warned. "He must still be around here. It hasn't been a week since he held a man up and almost killed him over Fabius way."

"I'll be at Fabius in another hour," William said. "I've made it this far, so I guess I'll make it the rest of the way."

When he and Trez were riding down the lonely road once more, William felt in his pocket for the small packet. It was still there. He tried to dismiss his fears. After all, what did he really have to fear? Who would attack the post rider and try to rob him?

Suddenly he pricked up his ears. Far in the distance he thought he heard the sound of a horse's hoofs. Some one must be in a hurry.

William rode on for a few more minutes. He

was not certain where the Dawes farm was, but he knew that it was only a couple of miles from Fabius. He should be able to deliver the packet to Mr. Dawes and still reach Fabius in time for supper and a good bed.

William yawned. He would be ready for both by the time he reached Fabius. Three hours of riding post was a long time.

Again the sound of a horse's hoofs came on the wind. William drew rein and listened. There was no doubt in his mind this time. A rider on horseback was approaching rapidly.

William looked about his uneasily. He would have thought nothing of the flying hoofs if he had not had that packet of money in his coat pocket. He would have thought nothing about it if he had not known a bandit had been in the neighborhood lately.

He felt for the revolver at his waist again. The touch of the smooth cold steel against his fingers made him feel better. Still, could he shoot a man down if he had to? He did not know.

His lips tightened. For a moment he felt much more like a boy than a man. Then he pressed his knees into Trez's sides. Her pace increased. At once William felt better.

He rose in his stirrups and glanced backwards. Suddenly, over the brow of a hill behind him, came a black horse, galloping fast. It was a

large powerful horse, and the man riding it—William's quick glance told him this—had a black patch over one eye. Jean Roddy! Could Jean Roddy be the bandit?

Without taking time to think about it, William pressed his knees deeper into his mare's sides. She shot forward like an arrow.

William was really frightened now. Those footsteps on the porch—Jean Roddy had been at the Curtis's. He probably had heard all that William had told Mr. Curtis. There was no doubt in William's mind as to what Roddy was after now!

William leaned forward over his horse's neck. "Run, Trez! Run!" he muttered.

Trez flew faster, and her hoofs struck sparks from the stones in the road.

As she sped along, William hoped she would not stumble as she had done once before, on that night so long ago in the blizzard, when they were chased by the wolves.

150

"This time it's a human wolf!" William thought grimly. "He's more dangerous than the others."

The boy and his horse were riding furiously. From time to time he glanced back over his shoulder. Each time his pursuer had gained a little.

If only he could reach the outskirts of Fabius! William thought. Jean Roddy would not dare to rob him there, so close to people.

William glanced around, then groaned. He knew this road by heart. Fabius lay about two miles farther on, but now there were only about four hundred yards between Lucifer and Trez. William knew that Roddy would overtake him before he could reach the town.

Suddenly a cabin rose up ahead on the right. If he could turn in there, get inside, and close the door behind him! William looked behind again. By now the distance between the two horses had shortened to three hundred yards.

Luckily for William, the gate to the yard was

open. He whirled Trez into the clearing and up to the door of the cabin. He leaped to the ground and flung the reins over her head. Then he threw open the door of the cabin and ran inside, leaving Trez in the yard.

An old man seated beside the fireplace looked up in surprise. "Who—who are you?" he asked in a quavering voice. "What do you want?"

"A robber is after me!" William cried. "I'm a government mail carrier, and a man is trying to rob the mail."

"A robber! You don't say!" The old man pulled himself to his feet and reached for an ancient rifle over the fireplace. His hands were shaking with age.

William's heart sank as he looked at the old man. Clearly, he could expect no help here. He ran back and barred the door just as Jean Roddy sprang to the ground outside.

"All right, Fargo!" Roddy shouted. "I know

what you're carrying. Throw out the Dawes packet and I'll be on my way."

"Dawes?" the old man quavered. "Dawes? Why, that's my name!"

Jean Roddy called again. "Throw it out if you know what's good for you, Fargo!"

William drew the revolver from the holster at his belt. The shape and coldness of it made him feel more like a man than a boy.

Old Micah Dawes laid down his rifle. "My hand is too unsteady," he said. "You'll have to get him, boy."

"I—I can't shoot a man," William said.

The old man laughed silently. "You don't have to hit him. Just scare him away."

Somehow his words gave William strength and courage. He stepped to the window and peered outside. Jean Roddy was standing before the door. William aimed at the ground behind him and pulled the trigger.

"Hey!" Roddy jumped to one side, but before he could do more William fired again, and then again. "Hey, watch out!"

Just then two horsemen came galloping into the yard. Roddy saw them and whirled to run for his horse, but they headed him off and caught him before he could reach it.

"Stop, Roddy!" one of them shouted, aiming a big pistol. "Stay where you are!"

The other man sprang from his horse. As William and the old man watched from the cabin, he tied Roddy's hands behind his back and led him over to the black stallion. The other man, pistol in hand, came toward the cabin.

William hurried to open the door.

"Was it you who shot at that black-hearted villain?" the tall, strong-faced man asked.

"Yes." William nodded his head.

"Then you have my thanks. It's a pity you did didn't hit him, though."

154

"I'm glad I didn't," William said. "I didn't even try. I just wanted to scare him away."

The man held out his hand. "Well, congratulations on that much. I'm the sheriff. You've saved me the trouble of tracking that trouble-maker any farther. I'll be on my way. I want to see that Jean Roddy sleeps in jail tonight."

William drew a deep breath. "I must be going, too. I have the rest of the mail to deliver." He reached inside his coat and pulled out the packet. "This is for you, Mr. Dawes. Your son wanted to be sure that it was delivered."

The old man pushed it away. "No, no!" he begged. "I don't want it. I'm a silly, stubborn old man. My son wanted to send it to the bank, but I wouldn't hear of it. I know that I shouldn't keep money in the house. Take it to the bank at Manlius for me."

William sighed. He had come through a good deal of danger for that packet. Now old Micah

Dawes had changed his mind about it and wouldn't accept it after all.

"Someone would kill me for that money if I kept it here," the old man said.

William's eyes met the sheriff's. What Micah Dawes said was true. Yet William was not due at Manlius again for four days.

"I'll take the money to the bank for him," the sheriff said. "I'll give him a receipt for it. Then I'll deposit it in his name at the Manlius bank. When he wants anything, he can just write an order on the bank."

"That's good of you," William said. "If you weren't here, I guess I would have to take it back to Manlius myself, sir." He turned to Mr. Dawes. "Here is your money. If you'll just sign this paper, that shows I delivered it——"

"Receipts! Receipts! Receipts!" the old man grumbled. "I don't know what the world is coming to these days."

The sheriff winked at William. The boy winked back at the sheriff. Micah Dawes was hard to please. Finally the packet was in the sheriff's saddle bag. William had his receipt, and the sheriff had given a receipt to old Micah. William put it in an old Bible on the table, where Mr. Dawes could find it.

Old Micah was sorry to see William and the sheriff and his deputy leave. "Haven't had so much excitement in years," he said.

William promised to stop and visit him on his next trip to Fabius. "I must go now, though," he said. He shook the old man's trembling hand. "The people in Fabius will be wondering what has become of me. They will be wondering even more what has become of their mail."

He smiled at Micah Dawes and said, in a tone that was half joking and half serious, "The mail must go through, you know."

Damon and Pythias

THE TRAIN from Syracuse had just puffed into Auburn, New York. The young station agent was watching his men unload the freight. He had taught them to move quickly and carefully.

Auburn was the end of the line. In a short time the puffing locomotive with its coaches would back onto the siding. Then it would turn around and start the return trip to Syracuse.

An anxious voice spoke behind young William Fargo, the agent. "Can you tell me when the stage for Geneva will be in? I'm in a hurry."

The agent turned to meet the eyes of another young man. William recognized him at once.

158

He was with Pomeroy and Company's Albany and Buffalo Express. William knew that he traveled back and forth to Buffalo every week.

The stranger held out his hand. "My name's Henry Wells," he said.

"And mine is William Fargo. I know you work for Pomeroy and Company."

The young man smiled. "I'm a partner in a small way," he said.

"Oh!" William was impressed. He had often admired the tall stranger as he stepped from the train to the waiting stage. William was not surprised that he was a partner in Pomeroy's.

"It's a small express business, but we're growing," Henry Wells went on. "I like most things about my job. The only part I don't like is the way I have to travel. I have to make three changes between Albany and Buffalo. It's a pity the train doesn't go all the way."

"It will someday," William told him. "Give it

time. After all, it hasn't been in business too long, you know."

Wells had been looking down the street for the overdue stage. He glanced back at the freight agent. "You seem very sure about it," he said. "I wish I were."

"I am," said William. "Travel is getting better every day. Why, I can remember when the Erie Canal——"

Henry Wells gave a whoop of joy. "Here comes the stage!"

He turned to two small kegs on the ground beside him. The stagecoach rolled up. The driver pulled on the reins and brought the horses to a stop before the station.

Pomeroy's man lifted one of the kegs to the baggage carrier on top of the stage and tied it with a long rope.

"Have one of your men hand me the other keg, will you, Fargo?" he said over his shoulder.

160

"I don't see one," William said. He lifted the keg and swung it into place beside the first.

Both he and Wells were breathing heavily from their exertions. The kegs were heavy. Henry Wells laid one hand on the door of the coach and looked up at the driver.

"I hope there won't be any more delays," he said. "I musn't miss my train at Geneva."

"You won't," the driver promised.

Wells was inside the stagecoach now. "Thanks, my friend," he called out to William.

The driver high on his seat cracked his whip. The vehicle began to move down the street.

The passenger inside thrust his head out the window. "Bet you can't guess what's in those kegs!" he called to William. "Oysters!"

Oysters! William's mouth flew open. Everyone knew that oysters must be served almost as soon as they came from the ocean. Buffalo was a long way from the ocean.

Henry Wells burst out laughing at the look on William's face. "When I come through again, I'll tell you how people liked them in Buffalo," he called as the stage turned the corner.

Four days later Henry Wells returned to Auburn and asked William to have dinner with him.

"I told you the other day that I'd be back to tell you how the people in Buffalo liked my oysters, and how I got them there fresh," he said. "Well, I'm a man who always keeps his promises, so here I am."

They were seated across from each other at a table in a restaurant in Auburn. William was enjoying himself. Henry Wells was an interesting person. He always had something new or amusing to tell.

"I wish you could have seen Jim Laidley's face when I delivered those oysters," Wells was saying now, with a chuckle. "He owns the best restaurant in Buffalo. Of course, he takes a great

deal of pride in what he serves there. He thought oysters just couldn't be brought all the way to Buffalo, but I showed him!"

"I'm surprised myself that you could do it," William said. "It must be all of two hundred and seventy or eighty miles from Albany to Buffalo, isn't it?"

Henry Wells nodded. "And don't forget the bad roads and poor transportation. I came here from Albany on the train. Then I took Sherwood's coach from here to Geneva and a train from there through Rochester to Batavia. Finally, I had a forty-mile ride on the worst roads in the state to Buffalo. It was quite a trip!"

"I don't know how you managed it," William told him.

Henry Wells laughed. "I used my head, that's how. Those oysters were taken from the shells and packed in ice before I left Albany. Even then they were an awkward load. But they would

164

have spoiled on the way without ice. In the shell they would have been too large and heavy to carry. As it was, I sold them for three dollars a hundred—and they advertised Pomeroy and Company nicely!"

William smiled. "No wonder you're a partner in Pomeroy's."

Henry Wells looked up. "You know, Fargo, I've heard some good reports about you. People tell me you never lose a piece of freight. You often work long after your men have gone home. You're always in a good humor, and you know how to get along with everybody."

William's face lighted up. "Now where did you hear all that?"

Wells leaned back in his chair. "Oh, I get around," he said with a smile. He looked hard at William. "How long are you going to be satisfied with a freight agent's job?"

William frowned. "It isn't so bad. At least,

it's better than carrying a mail route or working in a grocery store. My brother Jerome and I opened our own store about a year ago, but we didn't do any good. I lost what little money I had saved. Frankly, it was a relief to get out of that store. I couldn't bear to stay behind a counter all the time."

"So you like being a freight agent?"

William frowned again. "Well, not too much, but I haven't been married long. I have a wife to support, and we are expecting a baby soon."

Wells was silent for a moment. Then he said, "I see. Well, if you ever decide to make a change, look me up."

Several years later, in 1848, William Fargo and his wife Annie moved to Buffalo to live. When they were settled in their new home, William looked proudly around the parlor and then smiled at his wife.

"Do you like it?" he asked.

"Oh, yes!"

"Are you glad we moved to Buffalo?"

She nodded. "You don't belong in a little town, William. You were made for bigger things."

He patted her hand. "Be careful. You make my head swell."

She shook her head. "You're too big a man for anything like that."

William looked into the flames in the fireplace. "It was a lucky day for me when I met Henry Wells," he said.

"It was a lucky day for him, too," Annie answered quickly.

William laughed. "Let's just say we work well together. Wells and Fargo. It sounds good, doesn't it? People used to call us Damon and Pythias after those two ancient Greeks who were such good friends. We were good friends, too."

"You're still friends, even though you're not partners any more," she said.

"Yes, and I miss Henry," William said thoughtfully. "I suppose he felt he must move to New York City, but somehow I have a feeling we'll work together again. At any rate, he gave me a start in the express business."

"Do you remember how excited we were when he and Mr. Dunning asked you to be a partner in the express lines they were setting up from Buffalo to Detroit?" Annie asked.

"Do I! That hundred dollars I borrowed to put in the venture looked like a million!"

"Don't forget the wagon," she reminded him.

He smiled. "I'm not likely to forget that, either. There have been many changes since then. Mr. Dunning sold out. Then Henry sold out to William Livingston and me. Of course, he's still in the express business, but his office is in New York now. We still do business together in a way, too, because Livingston is his Buffalo agent. But somehow it isn't quite the same."

"No," Annie said, "it isn't quite the same."

Two years later, in 1850, seven men gathered around a table in a room at the Mansion House in Buffalo. They had gathered there from as far east as New York City and as far West as Cincinnati, Ohio. All of them were important men, known to hundreds of people in the communities in which they lived.

They were here to sign an agreement of partnership, forming a company to be known as the American Express Company. Three large express lines had decided to compete no longer. Now they were combining in one firm.

The signers of the agreement were Henry Wells and Johnston Livingston of New York City; John Butterfield of Utica, New York; James D. Wasson of Albany, New York; William A. Livingston of Cincinnati, Ohio; and William G. Fargo and James McKay of Buffalo.

When the others had left, William Fargo and

Henry Wells stayed on. The two old friends had much to talk about. They were happy to see each other again.

William leaned back and clasped his hands behind his head. "So we're partners once more."

Henry Wells nodded. "It's a good feeling, too. Don't you agree?"

"We're growing," William told him. "You and Butterfield have all the business between New York and Buffalo. The Livingstons and I work from Buffalo to points west."

"This new company of ours should teach Alvin Adams something," Wells said with a grin. "The Adams Express Company has too much of the express business for its own good. Adams is a rival with whom it's hard to deal."

"What about California?" asked William. "Since the discovery of gold out there, many people have been going west. Shouldn't we look into the matter?"

"We'll wait a while," Wells said. "There will be plenty of time to act later, when we know whether the gold is plentiful and people continue to move out there. California is a long way from New York."

"There's plenty of business here at home, too," William said. "I'd like to travel through Ohio, Indiana, Illinois, and Iowa to look things over. Maybe I'll see about some boats to run on the Illinois Canal. They could carry freight and passsengers from Chicago to the Illinois River and down to the Mississippi."

Henry Wells smiled. "This is better than being a freight agent, eh, William?"

Fargo nodded. "Or a cobbler? I believe you told me you repaired shoes once."

Henry rose to his feet and began pacing up and down the room. "What was that sentence you used to quote all the time?"

" 'Neither snow, nor rain, nor heat, nor dark-

171

ness, are permitted to obstruct their speed,'"
William answered promptly.

"That's how I feel about our express lines,"
Henry said. "In some circles I have the name—
and so have you—of being a cold-blooded business man. But money isn't everything, William. I
feel a keen interest in what we are doing. I can see
our lines stretching all over the country. Everything that is handed to us—money, jewelry,
packages, letters—will be delivered safely."

William's eyes shone. "We will sit in our offices in Buffalo and New York and through our
company know exactly what is happening
throughout the country. Our messengers will
travel thousands of miles to deliver the money
and the packages and the letters that have been
entrusted to us. They will meet danger, cold,
heat, rain, snow, sleet, blizzards—all kinds of
weather—but they will deliver their parcels,
whatever they might be."

172

Henry Wells nodded. "None of the forces you named will be—how does it go?—'permitted to obstruct their speed.'"

"None of them," William agreed.

The two friends smiled at each other as they left the room. Their faces glowed with eagerness and excitement, and they looked almost boyish as they planned their newest venture together.

Tales of a Grandfather

I⊤ ᴡᴀꜱ New Year's Day, 1900, in Buffalo, New York. The air was crisp and cold. The sun shone down on the city streets.

The big house where Jim and Jon lived had been quiet until the boys came downstairs. Now the library echoed with the noise of their shouting and running.

Once or twice Grandfather looked up over his spectacles, but he said nothing. He knew that growing boys must be noisy sometimes.

"Yip-pee!" Jon cried as he pretended to crack a long whip.

The two boys galloped the length of the library. They were pretending that they were riding on a stagecoach in the Old West. Jon was the "jehu," the driver. Jim was the Wells Fargo messenger, who was responsible for protecting the coach's valuable cargo. Jim had two toy pistols strapped to his belt. He would protect the cargo with his life.

Jon shaded his eyes with one hand and looked into the distance. Actually he saw the cook, Bridget, moving about in the kitchen, but he was good at pretending.

"Indians!" he exclaimed. "Ride for your life! They musn't capture us! Surely with six horses we can outrun them."

He whipped his team as hard as he could. Jim looked back. He had a pistol in each hand.

"Bang! Bang!" he cried. "I shot one!"

The boys raced through the room as if real Indians were chasing them. Grandfather put his fingers to his ears.

"Come here!" he ordered above the clatter.

At once the boys stopped, looking a little guilty. They came to stand in front of him.

"Children should be seen and not heard," Grandfather informed them.

His eyes twinkled. The boys knew that he did not mean what he said. He never stopped them from play unless they became too noisy. Jon looked at Jim, and Jim looked at Jon. Maybe the Old West did not belong in a library after all.

"Tell us a story, Grandfather," Jon urged.

"Please do," Jim added.

"All right," Grandfather said. These grandsons of his, aged eight and nine, made him feel almost young again.

The boys dropped down at his feet. They wanted to hear every word of his story.

"A long time ago a young man I knew went west," Grandfather began.

The boys looked at each other. They thought

176

they knew who the young man was, but they did not say anything.

"Those were the days!" Grandfather said. "Gold had just been discovered in California, and San Francisco was a busy place. Wagon trains were just beginning to cross the Rocky Mountains then, but most of the people who went west went by ship. They sailed clear around Cape Horn at the tip of South America or they crossed the Isthmus of Panama by land and then took another ship to San Francisco."

"Either way sounds mighty long," Jon said.

Grandfather laughed. "The distance seemed even longer in 1853. But the thought of gold led men on through all kinds of danger."

"I'd like to go to California someday," Jim said. "I'd like to see San Francisco."

Grandfather shook his head. "San Francisco won't look as it did then. When this young fellow first saw the town, its streets were crowded

day and night. Clipper ships thronged the harbor. Hotels were running over with people. When they went to eat, people paid three dollars for ham and eggs and a cup of coffee."

Jim held up his toy pistols. "Bang! Bang!"

The old man smiled. "Yes, you could hear guns almost any time. Stagecoaches set off every day with mail and supplies for the mines. Others returned every night with loads of gold dust. Excitement and adventure were everywhere."

"What did the young man do?" asked Jon.

"He went to Sacramento, the capital of California, and got himself a job," Grandfather replied. "The express business was booming then. There were several companies, competing with one another. The young man hardly knew which one to try. Luck was with him. He went with Wells, Fargo & Company."

Jim waved his pistols. "Bang! Bang! Wells Fargo never forgets!"

The corners of Grandfather's mouth twitched. "I see you've heard of the company."

"Everybody has heard of Wells Fargo."

"Sh-h-h," Jon said. "Go on, Grandfather."

"Well, the young man kept busy," Grandfather continued. "Every time the coach went out on its route, he went along as messenger.

"He sat high up on top of the coach beside the driver. He had a shotgun and knew how to use it, too. At his feet was a green wooden chest with wrought iron hinges. There was a metal plate on top of the chest with the words WELLS FARGO engraved on it. All the gold and other valuables with which the company had been entrusted were carried in that chest, and it was his duty to protect it."

"Did he ever shoot anyone?" asked Jim.

"Not unless a bandit tried to hold up the stage," Grandfather replied. "He knew he must defend that little green box that belonged to

Wells Fargo. No one ever lost a dollar in merchandise or gold that had been entrusted to the company. People could always depend on Wells, Fargo & Company."

"Who was the most famous bandit the young man ever saw?" Jon asked.

Grandfather thought a moment. "I suppose it was Joaquin Murieta. He was a handsome fellow with a soft voice and a pleasant manner."

"Didn't the young man kill him?" Jon asked again. He seemed disappointed.

"The West was a wild place in those days, but people shot others only in self-defense," Grandfather said. "No, the young man didn't shoot Joaquin Murieta. There was no reason to. He was doing nothing wrong at the time. Someone simply pointed him out on the street."

"It doesn't sound like such an exciting life," Jim remarked.

Grandfather looked amused. "Maybe not, but

you would have felt differently if you had been there. A stagecoach with its driver, its Wells Fargo messenger, and its passengers never gave up until it reached the end of its journey. And that journey was never easy. There were clouds of dust in summer, seas of mud in the rainy season, and snow-blocked trails in winter."

"Why did the young man keep on working for Wells Fargo then?" asked Jon.

Grandfather rubbed his chin. "He often asked himself that question. I think he and the others like him were too stubborn to give up. Then it was an exciting life, and the job paid well. The miners needed supplies and a safe way to carry their gold out of the mines, and they were willing to pay for such things. They could trust Wells Fargo messengers. Besides——"

He stopped and looked at the boys. They waited eagerly for him to continue.

"I'm not sure you would understand."

"Try us," Jon suggested.

"Well, the young fellow liked to feel that he was a part of a growing country," Grandfather went on, choosing his words carefully. "California was growing by leaps and bounds at that time. No sooner had the Gold Rush of '49 begun to die down than gold and silver were discovered in Nevada just over the border from California. They called that new field the Comstock Lode. The first one had been the Mother Lode.

"Everything started all over again with the Comstock Lode," Grandfather went on. "Virginia City sprang up on the side of Sun Mountain. There never was such a town before or since. Mark Twain was editor of a newspaper there. He called it the Virginia City *Enterprise.*"

"Was he the same Mark Twain who wrote *Tom Sawyer*?" Jon asked in surprise.

His grandfather nodded. "Twain wrote a book about his adventures during the gold rush. He called it *Roughing It*. You ought to read it some-day when you get a chance."

"I will," Jon said. "I liked Tom Sawyer."

"By the time the Comstock Lode was dis-covered Wells Fargo had acquired a strange name among the people of San Francisco," Grandfather went on. "It was called the Fat Cat of Montgomery Street. It was called that because it was prosperous and always managed to keep going when other express firms failed. Its main offices were on Montgomery Street, in down-town San Francisco."

"Why didn't it fail, too?" asked Jim.

"Well, it was owned by some very wealthy men back east," Grandfather said. "Besides that, these men also owned the American Express Company and weren't going to let Wells Fargo go under when times were bad.

"The two chief owners of Wells, Fargo & Com-pany were Henry Wells and William George

Fargo," Grandfather went on. "They started the company in 1852, after California became a state and it was clear that business would grow rapidly in the West. I've always thought myself that it was William Fargo's great business ability that kept Wells, Fargo & Company prosperous even in bad times."

"I suppose he hurried out to California to fix things whenever Wells Fargo was having trouble," Jon said.

"No," Grandfather said, shaking his head. "As a matter of fact, Mr. Fargo never went farther west than Omaha, Nebraska. He wasn't a miner or pioneer or adventurer. He was a business man, what we call a financier today. He was interested only in organizing and running a big business. But such men are very important. They have helped to make America great, just as men like Washington, Jefferson, and Lincoln have."

Jon looked unhappy. "All that fun—stagecoaches, green treasure chests, bandits, Indians, wrecks, fights—and he wasn't there to enjoy it!"

Grandfather laughed. "Oh, he enjoyed it in his own way, all right. Mr. Fargo enjoyed building his business empire. And he built well, too. Before long the name of Wells Fargo stood for safety and dependability throughout the West. And because people knew they could depend on it, the company grew and grew.

"In the beginning Wells Fargo messengers rode on the stagecoaches of other companies. In 1858, however, William Fargo and an old friend, John Butterfield, started the Butterfield Overland Express. This was a stage line to carry mail, freight, and passengers from St. Louis, Missouri, to San Francisco. The line extended 2,800 miles through Texas, New Mexico, and Arizona to California. Since the country wasn't settled, the company built way stations every eighteen miles or so along the route. Here the stage drivers could get fresh horses for their coaches, and the passengers could rest and eat."

"How did the company do?" asked Jim.

"It did very well until the Pony Express was started," Grandfather replied. "The Pony Express could carry a letter to San Francisco in ten and a half days while it took the Overland Express twenty days. So for a while most of the business went to the Pony Express.

"However, William Fargo was not a man to give up easily. He at once began to buy up stagecoach lines. He even bought out his partner John Butterfield until he owned all of the Butterfield company. Then he moved the Butterfield line farther north and nearer the Pony Express line. Meanwhile he got a contract from the government to carry government mail, and the Pony Express was in trouble. William Fargo had come out on top again."

"It was too bad the Pony Express could not

keep on running," Jon said. "It certainly must have been an exciting business."

"Yes, it was a great undertaking," Grandfather agreed. "It served a real purpose while it lasted. However, even if Wells Fargo had not forced it out of business, the telegraph line that was being completed across the country would have ended it. News traveled much faster over telegraph wires than the Pony Express riders could ever carry it."

"What became of the Pony Express?" asked Jim. "Did Wells Fargo take it over, too?"

"Not exactly," Grandfather replied with a smile. "They might have been thinking about it, but before they could move it was taken over by a man named Ben Holladay. Holladay was a shrew businessman who knew the stage business as well as the Wells Fargo people did."

"Which company was best?" asked Jim.

Grandfather shrugged. "Who can say? Both

companies had brave drivers and messengers who were afraid of nothing. The War between the States was being fought then, and as long as it lasted both companies were prosperous. In 1866, however, Wells Fargo bought Holladay out. When that happened, Wells Fargo owned all the principal stage lines in the West."

"I guess Wells Fargo really made money after that," Jon said. "Mr. Fargo and his friends must have been very happy."

"It made money, all right," Grandfather said. "It always did and always has. But its stage lines soon had competition which even they couldn't beat. In 1869 the first railroad across the country was completed near Ogden, Utah. Of course, a train could travel faster than a stage-coach and carry more."

"So that was the end of Wells Fargo!" Jim said.

"Oh, no!" Grandfather laughed. "Wells Fargo simply began to ship its express by train."

"I bet Mr. Fargo didn't like that!" Jon said.

"He believed in keeping up with the times," Grandfather said, a little sadly. "The day of the stagecoach were almost over, and he knew it. Of course, the messengers' life was still exciting, because the man who robbed the coaches now tried to rob the trains. But—" he shook his head— "the trains were not as exciting as those old red and yellow and black coaches.

"Maybe Mr. Fargo did lose interest, though. Just about this time he became mayor of Buffalo, New York, where he still lived. Then he bought a newspaper there. And he built a big house in Buffalo that cost half a million dollars."

"Half a million dollars!" Jon exclaimed. "Did you ever see it?"

"Yes, the only time I ever met Mr. Fargo was in that house. There was a chandelier in the drawing room which people said cost $10,000. I saw it with my own eyes."

"I guess that must have been the most exciting moment of your life," Jim said.

Grandfather shook his head.

"What was, then?" Jon demanded.

Grandfather stared at the floor for a moment. "I couldn't choose any one time," he said at last. "The happiest days of my life were the ones I spent in the messenger's seat of a Wells Fargo coach. Those were the days!"

"I wish I could have been a Wells Fargo messenger," Jim said wistfully.

"It sounds like an exciting life," Jon agreed.

"It was exciting," Grandfather said. "If I could live any part of life over, it would be those days when I rode on a Concord coach with a green Wells Fargo chest at my feet and a shotgun in my lap. I wouldn't have traded places with a king then. I thought there was no finer job in the world than being a Wells Fargo messenger."

More About This Book

WHEN WILLIAM FARGO LIVED

1818   WILLIAM FARGO WAS BORN ON A FARM IN NEW YORK, IN AUGUST.

There were 20 states in the Union.

James Monroe was President.

The population of the country was about 9,158,000.

1825   WILLIAM SAW THE OPENING OF THE ERIE CANAL WITH HIS FAMILY.

Jedediah Smith made the first overland journey to California, 1826.

Andrew Jackson was President, 1829-1837.

1830   WILLIAM FARGO BEGAN TO CARRY U.S. MAIL IN CENTRAL NEW YORK.

Peter Cooper built the first steam locomotive in the United States.

Cyrus McCormick invented the reaper, 1831.

Samuel Morse invented the telegraph, 1835.

American settlers reached Oregon, 1836.

1838– WILLIAM FARGO WORKED AS A FREIGHT AGENT
1850   AND IN THE EXPRESS BUSINESS.

The United States acquired the Oregon Territory south of the forty-ninth parallel, 1846.

The Mexican War was fought, 1846-1848.

1850   WILLIAM FARGO, HENRY WELLS, AND OTHERS
       ORGANIZE THE AMERICAN EXPRESS COMPANY.

California became a state.

The first overland mail was delivered from St. Louis to Salt Lake City.

1852   WILLIAM FARGO AND HENRY WELLS ORGANIZED
       WELLS, FARGO & COMPANY.

The first mail was delivered by Pony Express, 1860.

Abraham Lincoln was President, 1861-1865.

The War between the States was fought, 1861-1865.

The first transcontinental telegraph was completed, 1861.

President Lincoln was assassinated, 1865.

The first transcontinental railroad was completed, 1869.

1880 WILLIAM FARGO DIED IN BUFFALO, NEW YORK.

There were 38 states in the Union.

Rutherford B. Hayes was President.

The population of the country was about 50,155,000.

DO YOU REMEMBER?

1. Where did William Fargo's family live?
2. What was being celebrated the day the Fargos went to Pompey?
3. What did the Fargos go to Syracuse to see?
4. Who came to the Fargos' home one summer day and what did he have for a pet?
5. How did the peddler reward William for saving his wagon?
6. What did William do on the canalboat trip to Buffalo?
7. What happened after William and his father reached Buffalo?
8. How did William help to capture a pickpocket at Niagara Falls?
9. What did the grateful farmer give William?

10. Where did William spend his twelfth winter, and what happened to him there?

11. How old was William when he began to carry the U.S. mail?

12. How did William escape from the man who tried to rob him one day?

13. What was William doing when he met Henry Wells?

14. Where and how did William and Henry Wells go into business together?

15. In what year was the American Express Company founded, and who were the chief founders?

16. What caused Henry and William to organize Wells, Fargo & Company?

17. Where did Wells Fargo conduct its business?

18. What did William Fargo do in later years of his life?

IT'S FUN TO LOOK UP THESE THINGS

1. Who was DeWitt Clinton and what part did he play in the building of the Erie Canal?

2. How did peddlers do business when William Fargo was young?

3. How did the delivery of mail in the 1830's and 1840's differ from the delivery of mail today?

4. Why did the express business grow so rapidly in the 1830's and 1840's?

5. What became of the American Express Company which William and his friends organized?

6. What other famous express company competed with Wells Fargo in the West?

INTERESTING THINGS YOU CAN DO

1. Decide which chapter or chapters of the story you like best and write a play about them. Then choose several friends to help you present the play to the class.

2. Find pictures of canalboats, stagecoaches, express wagons, and trains of the years before the War between the States, when William Fargo was a young man. Bring the pictures to class for a transportation display.

3. Write a story about canalboating on the Erie Canal and read it aloud to the class. You may wish to find more information about the canal in reference books.

OTHER BOOKS YOU MAY ENJOY READING

California Gold Rush, May McNeer. Follett.

DeWitt Clinton: Boy Builder, Mabel Cleland Widdemer. Trade and School Editions, Bobbs-Merrill.

Erie Canal, Samuel Hopkins Adams. Trade Edition, Random House. School Edition, Hale.

Trails West and the Men Who Made Them, Edith Dorian and W. N. Wilson. Whittlesey.

We Were There at the Opening of the Erie Canal, Enid Meadowcroft. Grossett.

We Were There with the Pony Express, William O. Steele. Grossett.

INTERESTING WORDS IN THIS BOOK

agent (ā′jĕnt) : person who acts for another

anxious (ăngk′shŭs) : uneasy, worried

barges (bärj′ĕz) : roomy boats used for hauling people and freight on rivers or canals

bunting (bŭnt′ĭng) : thin woolen stuff used for flags and decorations

carpetbag (kär′pĕt băg′) : satchel or kind of suit-case made of carpet

clipper ship (klĭp'ẽr shĭp) : slender, fast sailing ship usually having three masts

cobbler: person who mends shoes

concert (kŏn'sûrt) : musical performance by one or more instruments

decent (dē'sĕnt) : free from anything bad; fairly good

dependability (dĕ pĕn'dȧ bĭl'ĭ tĭ) : state of being trustworthy

deposit (dĕ pŏz'ĭt) : place in a strong place as a bank for safekeeping

enabled (ĕn ā'b'ld) : made possible

feedbag: bag used for feeding horses which is fastened over the horse's head

financier (fĭn ăn sēr') : person who invests money in and runs businesses

flanks: sides

flares (flārz) : bright, blazing lights or torches

flattery (flăt'ẽr ĭ) : exaggerated praise; act of saying nice things about a person without really meaning them

flotilla (flȯ tĭl'ȧ) : small group of boats

horizon (hȯ rī'z'n) : point where earth and sky meet

199

isthmus (ĭs′mŭs) : narrow strip of land connecting two larger bodies of land

lavender (lăv′ĕn dēr) : pleasant-smelling oil made from the flowers of the lavender plant

lode (lōd) : mineral deposit, as of gold or silver

militia (mĭ lĭsh′à) : group of men organized as a military force for training but used only when needed badly

obstruct (ŏb strŭkt′) : stop or keep from passing

precipice (prĕs′ĭ pĭs) : steep or overhanging cliff

receipt (rĕ̇ sēt′) : piece of writing that says one has received or accepted something

represented (rĕp′rĕ̇ zĕnt′ĕd) : acted as agent for others in Congress or some similar body

sheepishly: timidly and foolishly

sinister (sĭn′ĭs tēr) : dishonest, evil, bad

stallion (stăl′yŭn) : male horse

talons (tăl′ŭnz) : strong, sharp claws of an eagle or other bird of prey

vehicle (vē′ĭ k'l) : wagon, automobile, or any other moving object used to transport things

wicker: anything made of osiers, the stems of a thin reedlike plant

200

BABE RUTH, *Van* ...
JIM THORPE, *Van* ...
KNUTE ROCKNE, ...
LOU GEHRIG, *Van* ... *s, Burt*

AUTHORS a...
COMPOSER...

ERNIE PYLE, *Wils*...
HARRIET BEECHER ...
  Widdemer
JAMES WHITCOMB ...
JAMES FENIMORE C...
JOHN PHILIP SOUS...
KATE DOUGLAS W...
LOUISA ALCOTT...
MARK TWAIN, ...
MARY MAPES D...
STEPHEN FOSTER... *oth*
WASHINGTON I... *er*

  Wilkie

A. P. GIANNINI...
JOHN WANAMA... **DERS**
  UR
EARLY   **ON**
SETTLERS...

JAMES OGLETHO...
MYLES STANDIS... *enson*
PETER STUYVESA...
VIRGINIA DARE...
WILLIAM BRADFORD, *Smith*
WILLIAM PENN, *Mason*

PAUL REVERE, *Stevenson*
TOM JEFFERSON, *Monsell*